THE HUMAN BODY'S
CABINET OF ETYMOLOGICAL CURIOSITIES

Written and illustrated by

John J. Kelway

First published in France by John Kelway in December 2020.

John Kelway
23 Rue Bergeon
Bordeaux, 33 800
France

kelwaybooks@gmail.com

Cover design and layout by Floriane Couture.

Typeset in Century Schoolbook 9 pt.

ISBN 978-2-9574847-0-6

To all four of my grandparents. Thank you for everything.

PREFACE

Cabinets of curiosities were private collections of curious objects that were put together by aristocrats, rich merchants and travellers. They would contain anything from stuffed animals, to stones, to religious objects and archaeological relics. More fantastical things like unicorns' horns, vampires' teeth, mummified monsters and fairies' skeletons were often displayed as well.

Over the centuries, the human body has assembled its own collection of curiosities, as generation after generation of anatomists have named body parts after animals, plants, tools, and weapons. These things are not in themselves curious, but it is indeed curious to find them inside the human body. *The Human Body's Cabinet of Etymological Curiosities* is a collection of pencil drawings that depict the etymology of anatomical terms. These "etymogrammes" represent anatomical structures and the etymological origins of their names. Each illustration is accompanied by a short paragraph that explains the origin of the term, and supplies the reader with interesting information about the anatomical structure in question. Some etymologically related words are given to show how modern English is riddled with Greek and Latin roots that help to understand and remember the names of our body parts. Sometimes, the information may stray a little off topic, but that is the beauty of a cabinet of curiosities: you never know what you might find inside.

Throughout the pages of this book, too little credit is given to the ancient physicians who first explored the human body and named many of its structures. Here is perhaps the place to acknowledge their work, without which this book would not exist. The illustrations in this book are not the fruit of my own imagination, but seek to represent what these early anatomists might have had in mind when they named the structures of the human body. Although a great many anatomists have left their mark in the anatomical lexicon, a special mention must go to two historical masters of anatomy, Galen and Vesalius. The first was a second century Greek physician who was a doctor to the gladiators. He gained his knowledge of anatomy by dissecting and vivisecting primates and pigs, since human dissection was forbidden at the time. He wrote several books that remained the uncontested foundations of anatomy for over a millennium, even though they contained countless errors that resulted from extrapolating observations made in animals to humans. It was only in the sixteenth century that the Flemish anatomist Andreas Vesalius dared to contradict some of Galen's observations. Vesalius dissected humans, and so was able to challenge many misconceptions, like the belief that women had fewer ribs and teeth than men.

He wrote a ground-breaking set of seven books called *De Humani Corporis Fabrica* which he illustrated himself with beautiful, artistic renderings of his dissections, as shown in the illustration on the opposite page.

After Vesalius, the field of anatomy grew rapidly, and so did its vocabulary. By the 19th century there were so many different ways of designating each anatomical structure that in 1895 an international committee finally decided that it was about time they agreed on what things should be called. They wrote a lexicon called the *Nomina Anatomica*, a list of internationally recognised anatomical terms, which were mainly in Latin and Latinised Greek. This reduced the total number of anatomical terms in use from over 70, 000 to about 5, 000. Before the consensus, there were about 50 synonyms for the pineal gland alone for instance. Since the first edition was published in 1895, the *Nomina Anatomica* has been updated and revised several times. The latest update was published in 1998 and is called the *Terminologia Anatomica*. There is a Latin version of the *Terminiologia Anatomica* and an English version, but the English version contains as much Latin as English.

The universal language of anatomy set out in the *Terminologia Anatomica* allows people to communicate no matter what country they come from and no matter what language they speak. On the downside, nobody actually speaks ancient Greek or Latin anymore, except for a few odd specimens who would deserve to be displayed in a cabinet of curiosities themselves. This means that students spend a lot of time learning the Latin and Greek names of body parts without actually knowing why they were given that name in the first place. As Tatsuo Sakai, a Japanese anatomist, wrote in an article published in 2007, "Anatomical terms are very convenient tools for describing and identifying anatomical structures but (...) medical students frequently feel that anatomical terms are a heavy burden to their memory". If you are, were or want to become a medical professional, understanding the origins of anatomical vocabulary makes that vocabulary much more meaningful. This makes learning anatomy both a lot easier and much more fun.

Most books on the etymology of anatomical terms are academic works intended for medical professionals and students alone. This book differs in that it aims to be an entertaining art book/coffee table book/toilet book that can be enjoyed by both specialists and non-specialists alike. If you are already interested in anatomy, I hope this book will stoke the fire of your curiosity. If, on the other hand, you do not know the first thing about the human body, I hope this book will ignite that fire. Finally, even if you are not interested in reading the text, you can always just look at the pictures.

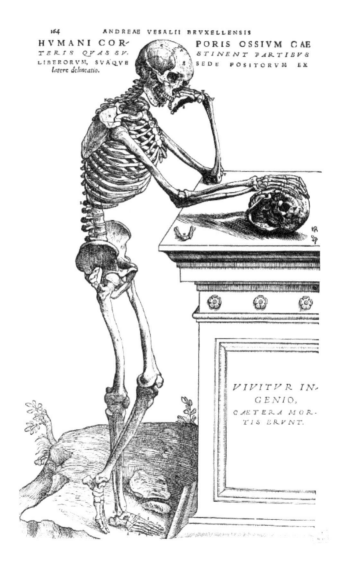

An illustration from Andreas Vesalius's
De Humani Corporis Fabrica, *1543.*

The Human Body's
Cabinet of Etymological Curiosities

THE ACETABULUM

The hip joint is a ball and socket joint that links the head of the femur (the ball) to the *acetabulum* of the pelvis (the socket). In Rome, an *acetabulum* was a small rounded vinegar cup, from the Latin *acetum* for "vinegar" and *abulum* for "small cup or vessel". An acetabulum was used as a unit of measurement for liquids by Roman doctors, much as cooks use cups to measure out their ingredients today. The resemblance between the hip socket and the little measuring cup probably sprang quite naturally to mind when they examined the bones of the hip.

At the bottom of the acetabulum there is another, smaller cavity called the *cotyloid fossa*. *Cotyloid* comes from the Greek *kotule*, which also means "cup". So there is another cup at the bottom of the vinegar cup, which itself is a part of the pelvis. Perhaps the pelvis is yet another cup, making a cup in a cup in a cup? Go to the chapter on the pelvis to find out.

The acetabulum can be fractured in what is known as a "dashboard fracture" that often results from being thrown forward during a car accident, causing the knee to strike the dashboard of the car. The head of the femur (the thighbone) is forced backwards into the acetabulum, resulting in a break in the posterior rim of the acetabulum. Unfortunately, you cannot just superglue the acetabulum back together as you would the broken pieces of a vinegar cup.

Related words

The acid in vinegar is known as acetic acid.
Acetone is the active ingredient in nail polish remover and paint thinner. Chemists used to make acetone out of vinegar and lead. You can make it at home out of vinegar and eggshells as well.
Acetone belongs to a group of substances called ketones, a word that shares the same origin. "Ketogenic" is a word that has recently become more well-known thanks to the fitness and weight-loss industries, which have popularized ketogenic diets (originally designed to treat epilepsy). These high-fat, low-carb diets are designed to make you burn fat rather than sugar as an energy source. When the liver rapidly breaks down fat, ketone bodies are produced, hence the term "ketogenic".

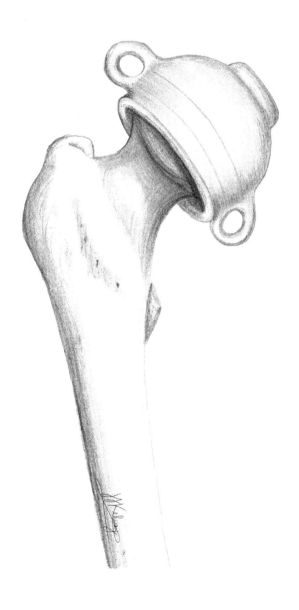

THE ACHILLES TENDON

The Achilles tendon is the thick cord that attaches your calf muscles to the back of your heal bone. Or as anatomists would put it, it is the thick bundle of dense fibrous connective tissue connecting the *gastrocnemius* and *soleus* to the posterior aspect of the *calcaneus*. All three of these words *gastrocnemius*, *soleus* and *calcaneus*, have interesting origins. *Gastrocnemius* contains the same *gastro* as gastroenteritis, and literally means "the belly of the leg". The technical term for the heel bone is the *calcaneus* or *os calcis,* words that share the same origin as calcium and calculus. They are derived from the Latin *calx*, meaning "chalk" or "pebble". "What is the link between calculus and pebbles?" I hear you ask. Pebbles were in fact once used as extra fingers for counting and calculating. And finally the *soleus* is lucky enough to have a whole chapter all to itself.

Achilles was the greatest of all the Greek warriors who fought during the Trojan war according to Homer's Iliad. Achilles was said to be invincible because his mother, the nymph Thetis, dipped him in the river Styx, which separates the Earth from the Underworld, when he was a baby. This rendered him totally invulnerable ... except that when his mother dipped him in the magical waters, she held him by his ankle. Thus, his heel was not exposed to the wonderful waters of the Styx, and became his single weak spot. Unfortunately, after having become the hero of the Trojan war by killing Hector and dragging his corpse around behind a chariot (heroes managed their public image differently in those days), Achilles was shot by Paris, right in the heel, and died. To this day, someone's "Achilles heel" is a metaphor for their weak spot. So funnily enough, you could say that the Achilles tendon is actually the Achilles heel of many runners, who tend to damage this tendon.

Related words

Achillesaurus was a dinosaur with remarkable heels.
Achilles syndrome is a psychological state characterized by a fear of being found out as a fraud, because you think that your seemingly advanced skills are actually built on fragile foundations.

THE AMYGDALA

There are many nuts, grains, fruits and legumes in the body. In the brain, there are at least two: the amygdala and the pineal gland. The name amygdala comes from the Greek *amygdale*, meaning "almond". These two almond-shaped structures are involved in memory consolidation and emotional responses such as fear and anxiety.

Our understanding of the brain owes much to a small number of patients who have lost, in some way or another, a part of their brain. If a specific part of your brain is missing and as a consequence you are utterly unable to accomplish a certain task or display a certain emotion, it is proof that that part of the brain plays a major role in that task or emotion. The field of neuroscience is greatly indebted to several such patients who are usually referred to by their initials: patient H. M., patient S. M., patient K.C., etc. Phineas Gage is another famous patient who lost part of his brain, but was lucky enough to retain his full name.

Patient S.M. is an American woman whose amygdala were both destroyed by a disease she contracted as a child. Ever since, she has been unable to experience most forms of fear. You might think this a cool superpower to have, but we experience fear for a reason. Patient S. M. has been held at gunpoint and at knifepoint and has got herself into several life-threatening situations because of her inability to recognise and avoid potentially dangerous situations. One thing that does induce a fear response in patient S. M. is breathing in carbon dioxide, something scientists make people do on a regular basis to mimic the effects of suffocation. They do not do this to assuage their sadist desires, but as a way of studying how people respond to fear.

Related words

Amygdalin is a chemical found in bitter almonds, but also in the seeds of apples and greengages. Amygdalin is cyanogenic, because after ingesting the molecule, your body turns it into cyanide. For those who have already begun evolving diabolical schemes, well over a hundred apple seeds are required to induce cyanide poisoning in an average sized human. Amygdalin has become one of the best-known money-spinners in the history of medical quackery, ever since it was marketed as an anti-cancer drug under the name "Vitamin B17".

The word "**amygdala**" used to designate the tonsils, and still does in some languages such as French.

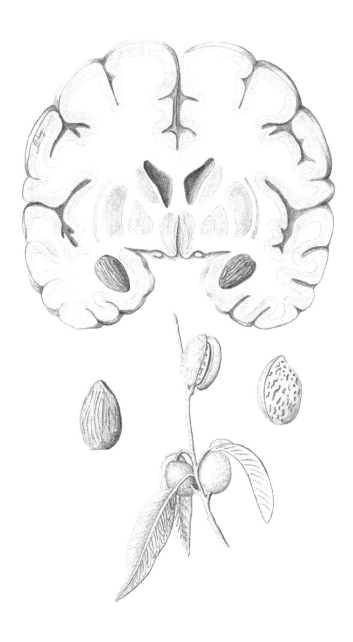

THE ANTRUM

The digestive system contains a wealth of interestingly named organs. Let us see what happens when you bite off a piece of healthy multigrain brown bread and start chewing. Your *incisors* quite literally cut through the hard crust like a knife. The word "incisor" comes from the Latin *incidere*, which means "to cut or slice". Your sharp *canines* dig in and allow you to tear a piece from the rest of the loaf, like a dog (a canine) ripping a morsel of meat from its unlucky prey. Your *molars* are perfect for grinding up the sesame, flax and sunflower seeds on your rustic baguette. The word "molar" comes from the Latin *mola*, which means "millstone". The resulting ball of mush gets pushed down your oesophagus, and falls into your stomach, where it is further mushed and mashed and generally mistreated.

Before leaving the stomach and entering the first part of the small intestine, the duodenum, your food must brave the *antrum*. The word *antrum* is Latin for "cave". It is a dark and dangerous cave, for here your food receives a final churning and burning before beginning its descent into the bowels. In English, an "antre" is also an archaic word for a cavern or cave. In other languages such as French, the word "antre" is still used for "cave". In the illustration, someone has excavated the abdominal wall and gained access to the antrum, the darkest part of the cave where stalactites and stalagmites can be seen.

More generally in anatomy and biology, an antrum is any cavity or hollow chamber in the body. There are a number of other antra beside the gastric antrum of the stomach: there are mastoid antra near the inner ear, there are follicular antra in the ovaries, and there are maxillary antra, another name for the sinuses beneath your eyes.

There is also another set of caves with a different etymological origin. The *corpora cavernosa*, literally the "cavernous bodies", are caverns that are usually empty, but fill up with blood during an erection. Both men and women have corpora cavernosa, men in the penis, women in the clitoris. Incidentally, the origin of the word clitoris is uncertain, but it could mean "little hill", "key", "tickle", or "touch lasciviously".

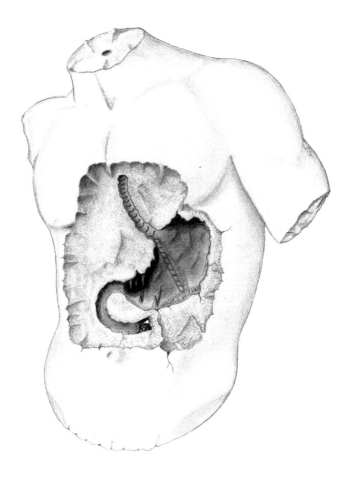

THE ARACHNOID MEMBRANE

This illustration shows a slice of the human skull and brain. The brain is separated from the skull by three membranes called the *meninges*. The closest to the brain is called the *pia mater* (the "tender mother") and the closest to the skull is called the *dura mater* (the "tough mother"). In between the two lies the *arachnoid membrane*, so called because of its cobweb-like structure. *Arachne* means "spider" in Greek, and there is a myth that explains how spiders came to be known as *arachne*.

Arachne was a young woman with a great talent for weaving. She took immense pride in her work. Perhaps too much, for she compared her skill to that of Athena herself, the patron goddess of weaving. Like all Gods, Athena disliked being rivalled by a mere mortal. Athena challenged Arachne to a weaving contest to see who could produce the most beautiful tapestry. Once they had both finished their work, Athena surveyed Arachne's tapestry looking for faults. To her dismay, the workmanship was perfect. If there was one thing the gods disliked more than being rivalled by a mortal, it was being beaten by one, so Athena threw a godly tantrum and tore up Arachne's tapestry and broke her loom. Arachne attempted to commit suicide by hanging herself, but the goddess was not going to let her get away with it that easily. Athena saved the young woman from the noose, and turned her into a spider to teach her an unforgettable lesson. Arachne got to keep her extraordinary skill at weaving, and gained six legs and six eyes in the process. After that, spiders came to be known as *arachne*.

Related words

Arachnophobes and **arachnophiles** are the sensible people who are scared of spiders and the senseless people who are fond of them, respectively.

Arachnogenic means caused by the bite of a spider. Spiderman's powers are arachnogenic for instance.

Arachnodactylia is a condition in which the fingers are abnormally long and slender, like spider's legs

Arachnomancy is the study of spiders or the patterns of their webs for use in divination.

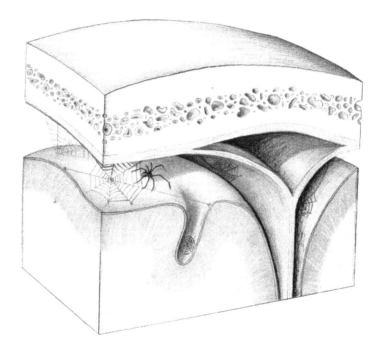

THE ARCUATE LIGAMENT

There are several *arcuate* and *arciform* structures throughout the human body: in the knee, the elbow, the groin, the diaphragm, etc. The illustration represents the arcuate popliteal ligament at the back of the knee. They were named *arcuate* or *arciform* (which means the same thing) because they are arch-shaped or bow-shaped. In Latin, *arcus* means "bow", but later on it also came to mean an "arch". Thus, we do not really know whether anatomists gave these ligaments their names because they thought they looked like bows or like arches (or perhaps both).

There is a structure in the brain called the *fornix*, which also means "arch" in Latin. It arches round a structure called the *thalamus*, the "bridal chamber" or "bed" of the brain. Sensory information from the eyes, ears, tongue and skin comes to rest in this bed before moving on to the cerebral cortex. But what good is a bed without a nice fluffy pillow? The thalamus is divided into thirteen groups of neurons, one of which is called the *pulvinar*, or "pillow".

As we can see, quite a few body parts are named after architectural structures. We have just mentioned the arcuate ligaments, the thalamus, and the fornix, but there are also the *pons* ("the bridge"), the *atria* ("open central room or court"), the *scalae* ("the staircases"), the *tectum* ("the roof"), the *vestibule* ("the antechamber, entrance, or lobby"), the *fenestrae* ("the windows"), the *septa* (the "hedges or fences"), etc.

Related words

Archery is the use of a bow for sport or hunting by an archer. Interestingly, bishops in the game of chess were once called archers. Maybe this is why they can move all the way across the board and take an opponent, as if they were shooting an arrow.
Archerfish are an amazing species of tropical fish that shoot arrows of water from their mouths in order to bring insects down from the air into the water. They can shoot their prey with unbelievable precision from more than a foot away. Check it out, it is worth it.

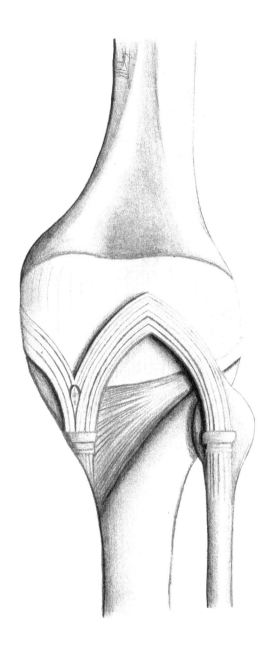

ATLAS

Atlas is another name for the first cervical vertebra (or C1). It is the very first bone of the spine that carries the skull. If you already know the role Atlas plays in Greek mythology, you will understand why early anatomists gave the bone its name.

Atlas was one of the Titans, the generation of Greek gods that preceded the Olympians (the Olympians being the more famous gods who were ruled by Zeus). The Titans fought against the Olympian gods during a ten-year war known as the Titanomachy. The Titans lost and were replaced by the Olympian gods as supreme rulers of the world. Being immortal, none of the Titans were actually killed during this war. Instead, many were sentenced to spend eternity in Tartarus, the dungeon of the Underworld. Atlas however was sentenced to hold up the heavens for all eternity. Nowadays we tend to think of Atlas as holding up the Earth, but in fact he held up the celestial orb (the sky).

Just as Atlas the Titan supports the celestial sphere for all eternity, atlas the cervical vertebra supports the cranial sphere for as long as we live. Atlas sits on top of the second cervical vertebra, axis, which you can find out more about in the chapter on the odontoid process.

Related words

The Atlas mountains are named after the Titan because according to some, he has been holding up the heavens for so long that he has turned to stone.
The Atlantic Ocean is the great sea beyond the place where Atlas stands.
Atlantis is the utopian fictional island described by Plato, that could well be hidden beneath the Atlantic ocean.
A collection of maps became known as an atlas since the famous cartographer Gerardus Mercator used an image of Atlas holding up the celestial sphere as a frontispiece on many of his maps.
In psychology, Atlas syndrome or Atlas personality is characterised by someone who is worn down by constant stress and responsibility.

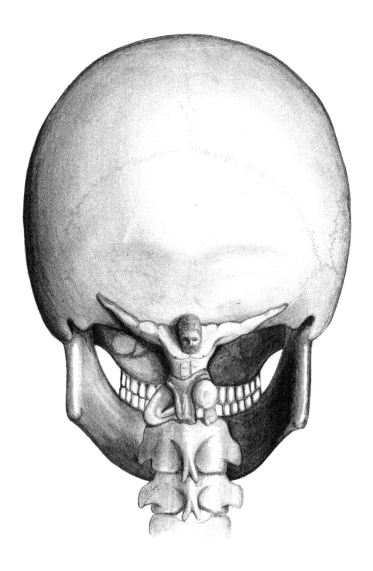

THE BUCCINATOR

Several bits and bobs in the human body have musically-inspired names: the tympanic membrane, the tibia, the salpinges, and of course the *buccinator*. A *bucina* was a kind of Roman horn or trumpet, as shown in the illustration. A *bucinator* (with one -c) was the person who played this instrument. Roman anatomists realised that the thin flat muscle of the cheek (the darker muscle in the illustration) was one of the muscles that allowed these musicians to build up enough pressure in their mouths to produce a sound with their *bucina*. The *buccinator* muscle gained its second -c as a mistake made by later scholars who wrongly assumed that the word had the same origin as *bucca*, which means "mouth or cheek" in Latin.

Salpinx is another trumpet-related anatomical term. There are two salpinges in the human body. The pharyngotympanic tube is a salpinx which allows you to maintain equal air pressure on either side of the ear drum. This tube opens up when you yawn for example, helping to unblock your ears on an aeroplane or when you are travelling up a mountain. The Fallopian tubes (that link the uterus to the ovaries) are also referred to as salpinges. A *syrinx* was another kind of musical instrument, a kind of panpipe which gave us the word "syringe".

There are a number of other interestingly named muscles in the face. For instance there is the simply yet aptly named *Levator Labii Superioris Alaeque Nasi* muscle. Despite its name, this muscle is unrelated to Nazis, but it *is* related to the king of rock and roll. It is the muscle Elvis Presley used to produce his hallmark facial expression, and has earned the nickname "Elvis muscle", although I do not know what is wrong with *Levator Labii Superioris Alaeque Nasi*. It literally means "the muscle that lifts the top lip and the nostrils".

The *risorius* muscle is the muscle that pulls the corners of the mouth outwards, creating a wide yet artificial party smile. *Risorius* comes from the Latin *risus* meaning "to laugh". This is rather unfair, because the muscle we use when we are really enjoying ourselves is the *zygomatic* muscle, although a true smile is not the work of a single muscle, but the combined activity of several muscles acting on the lips, cheeks and eyes all at the same time.

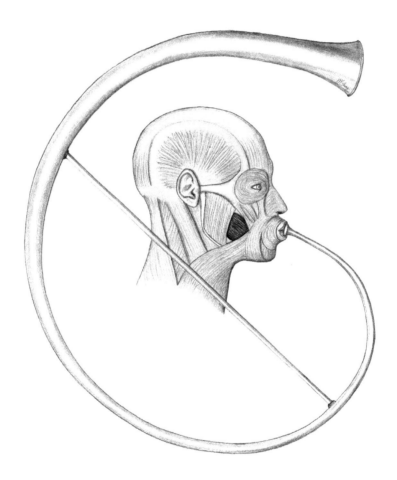

BURSAE

Bursae are little pouches filled with a kind of lubricant called synovial fluid. These pouches allow muscles, tendons and ligaments to slide over each other without producing too much friction. In Latin, a *bursa* means "a small leather pouch". You have many bursae all over your body. The bursa shown in the illustration is the subacromial bursa of the shoulder joint. Overuse can cause inflammation of the bursae, a condition called bursitis. Some forms of bursitis have been given interesting names. Prepatellar bursitis is called Housemaid's Knee, a condition that you can get by kneeling down a lot. If you have read Jerome K. Jerome's "Three Men in a Boat", you might remember that housemaid's knee is the only condition in the medical dictionary from which the narrator does not suffer. Infrapatellar bursitis, another condition that you can get from kneeling a lot, is known as Clergyman's or Preacher's Knee. Members of the clergy obviously kneel differently to housemaids. Iliotibial bursitis is known in French as Window-Wiper Syndrome ("syndrome de l'essui-glace") because when you run, the iliotibial band rubs back and forth over the lateral epicondyle of the knee, like a window-wiper.

Besides the bursae, there are other leather bags and pouches in the body. There are for instance the saccule and the utricle in the inner ear. "Saccule" comes from *sacculus*, the diminutive of *saccus*, meaning "a sack" in Latin. "Utricle" comes from *utriculus*, the diminutive of *uter*, meaning "a leather bag". These little bags contain crystals called *otoliths* (literally "ear stones") that help you to determine if your head is straight or leaning to one side. Follicles are yet more little bags (from the diminutive of *follis*, "money-bag" in Latin). We all have hair follicles and women have ovarian follicles as well.

Related words

Bursa gave us the word "**purse**", in both senses: the noun (the pouch for money) and the verb "to purse", because when you purse your lips, the skin wrinkles like the leather of an old-fashioned pouch with the drawstring pulled tight.
A **bursar** is the treasurer of a university, and a **bursary** is a student's grant that does not need to be **reimbursed**.
In French, *bursa* gave "**bourse**", which is another word for the scrotum. Funnily enough, it is also the French word for the stock market.

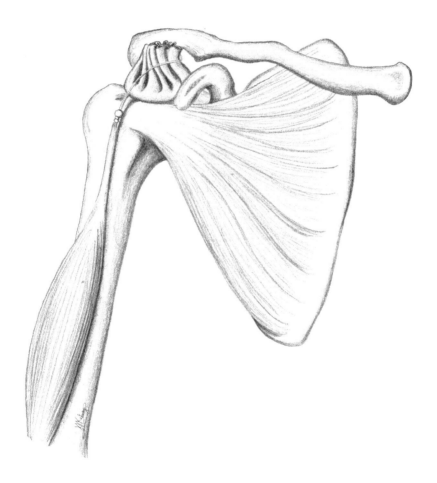

THE CAPITATE BONE

Caput, the Latin word for "head", has been used in the names of several structures throughout the body. There is for example the *capitulum* (also called the *capitellum*), the "little head" which is part of the elbow joint. There are also muscles that attach to and move the head, such as the *splenius capitis* and the *longus capitis*. And of course there is the *capitate* bone, the largest and most central of the eight carpal bones of the wrist, as shown in the illustration. The eight bones of the wrist are roughly arranged in two rows of four. The first row contains, from left to right, the roughly triangular *triquetrum*, the pea-shaped *pisiform*, the half-moon shaped *lunate* bone and the boat-shaped *scaphoid*. The second row consists of the hooked *hamate* bone, the *capitate* bone, the *trapezoid* and the *trapezium*. Several of these bones have entire chapters dedicated to them throughout the book.

The Greek word for "the top of the head", *kranion*, has given us several anatomical terms as well. The *cranium* is the upper part of the skull that encloses and protects the brain. *Cranial* is an adjective used in anatomy that means "towards the head". The *olecranon*, literally "the head of the elbow", is the sharp bony tip of the elbow. If you take a close look at Popeye, you will see that he not only has remarkable forearms and a memorable face, he also has very well-developed olecrana.

Related words

The **capital** city is the head of a country.
A **captain** is the head of a military unit or the head of a ship.
To **decapitate** is to remove the head from the body.
A **chapter** is the paragraph or section under a given heading.
The Latin word *caput* was exported to France and, over the years, became "chef". "Chef" came to mean an "end" (as in an intention or a goal). "Venir à chef" meant to accomplish, and "à chef" gave us "**achieve**". "**Chief**" shares the same origin.

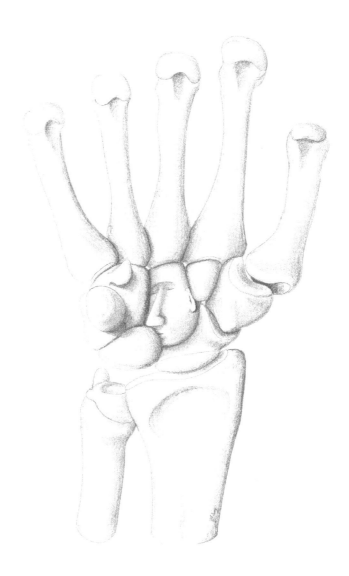

THE CAUDA EQUINA

The cauda equina is a bundle of nerve roots at the end of the spinal cord. The spinal cord emerges from the brainstem, travels down through the spinal canal formed by the vertebrae. All the way down, spinal roots emerge from the spinal cord and leave the spinal canal through a hole formed by two adjacent vertebrae. The spinal cord itself ends between the 1st and 2nd lumbar vertebrae, roughly at the top of the lower back. Beneath that, only the nerve roots continue downwards, leaving plenty of space in the spinal canal for doctors to perform lumbar punctures, known colloquially as spinal taps, without risk of damaging the spinal cord. A spinal tap is the act of removing a sample of cerebrospinal fluid, *i.e.* the fluid in which the brain and spinal cord bathe.

When early anatomists saw this bundle of nerve fibres at the end of the spinal cord, they were reminded of a horse's tail, or *cauda equina* in Latin. Cauda Equina Syndrome is a condition where the nerve roots of the cauda equina get compressed, leading to a gradual loss of feeling and motor function affecting the legs, the anus, and the urinary and genital systems. Coincidentally, the numbness that results from cauda equina syndrome affects the areas that would be in contact with the saddle if you rode a horse. This specific kind of numbness is known as "saddle anaesthesia", making it a doubly horsey disorder.

There is another structure in the central nervous system that takes its name from the Latin word for tail: the *caudate nuclei*. The caudate nuclei are structures deep within the brain that are classically defined as being C-shaped, with a head, a body and a long tail. The caudate nuclei are well-known for their involvement in Parkinson's disease.

Related words

Caudal is an adjective that means "related to the tail". It is used in anatomy to describe anything that is towards the tail, or towards the lower or back end of the body. It is the opposite of cranial.
Cauda was one of the many slang names Romans had for the penis.
The adjectives "**equine**" and "**equestrian**" should not be confused. Equine means related to the horse family, whereas equestrian means related to horse-riding.
Nowadays, "**inequitable**" means unfair, from the Latin *aequus* meaning equal. An archaic sense of the word inequitable was "impossible to ride over on horseback", from *equus*, meaning "horse".

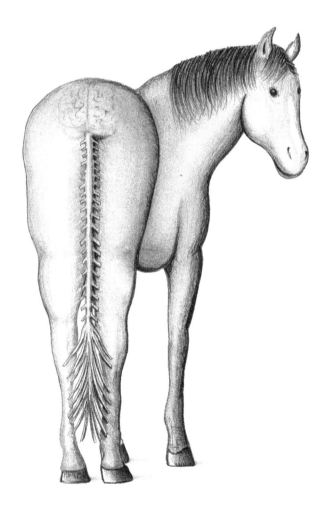

THE CLAVICLE

In Latin, *clavicula* is the diminutive of *clavis*, meaning a "key" or a "bolt". Some people think that the technical name for the collarbone derives from the role the clavicle plays in fastening the upper limb to the rest of the body. The most commonly held view seems to be that the clavicle resembles a little Roman key, which admittedly were more clavicle-shaped than our modern keys. The bone also resembles a key because it turns on its axis when you raise your arm, like a key turning in a lock. Others think that the name comes from a third sense of the Latin word *clavicula*, "tendril". They argue that the clavicle winds its twining course between the sternum and the acromion like the tendril of a climbing plant.

When you are born, you have about three hundred bones, whereas by the time you become an adult, you only have about 206. This is because some bones start off as cartilage and later turn into bone (like the kneecap for instance). Other bones begin with bony segments separated by cartilaginous segments. These cartilaginous segments gradually ossify, causing the bony segments to fuse together, leaving you with fewer bones in total.

Although the clavicle is the first bone in the body to begin to ossify in the womb, it is also the last bone in the human body to ossify completely. The clavicle has usually completely turned into bone by the age of 20 to 25. Since cartilage is a lot weaker than bone, this is one of the reasons why so many teenagers and young adults tend to break their collarbones.

Related words

The name **Cleopatra** is thought to mean "the key to the fatherland".
A **clavis** is another word for a glossary or a lexicon (the "key" to a text).
A **claviger** is a keeper of keys or key-holder.
In English, a **clavier** is the keyboard of a musical instrument. In French it is also a computer keyboard.

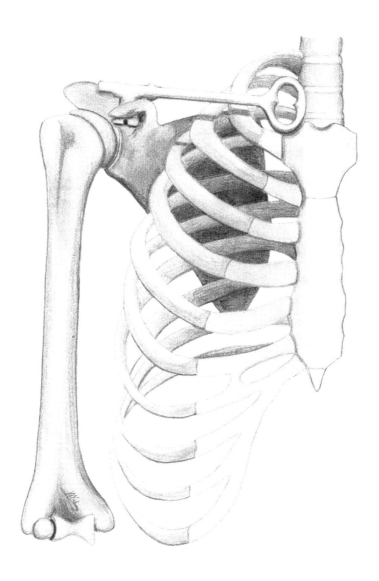

THE COCCYX

The coccyx is the very lowest and smallest part of the spine, comprising between 3 and 5 vertebrae. These vertebrae are usually separate when we are young, and gradually fuse together over the years. Viewed from the side, the coccyx is a curved, pointy structure resembling the beak of a bird. The discerning anatomists who named the coccyx thought it specifically resembled the moderately curved bill of a cuckoo. The Greek word for cuckoo was *kokkux*, probably an onomatopoeic word resembling the bird's cry. The illustration shows the head of a cuckoo at the base of the sacrum. Unfortunately, when you put the head of a cuckoo on a long neck, it looks more like a swan than a cuckoo.

The coccyx is a vestigial tail that has gradually shrunk over hundreds of generations from lack of use and attractiveness. This is why the coccyx is commonly referred to as the "tailbone". When you fall on your coccyx and the pain prevents you from sitting down for several days or weeks, you are suffering from coccydynia (a pompous word for a pain in the arse).

The English word "cuckold", meaning a man whose wife is unfaithful, comes from the name of the bird. Indeed, female cuckoos famously lay their eggs in the nests of other birds, a behaviour known as brood parasitism. The cuckoo's eggs are either accepted by the host as their own, in which case the egg will hatch and the chick will be fed by the host at the expense of the host's true offspring until it grows to several times the size of the adult host, or the egg will be identified as a parasite and discarded from the nest. This has led to what is known in biology as an evolutionary arms race, where the host and the parasite evolve more and more effective ways of outsmarting each other. As a result, the cuckoo's eggs have become more and more similar to their hosts' eggs, and the hosts have evolved eggs bearing more and more complex patterns so that they can be identified more reliably, a bit like a money forger and a banker constantly trying to outwit each other.

Not all cuckoos are brood parasites. Roadrunners are a non-parasitic species of cuckoo that contrary to popular belief do not say "Meep Meep", but rather "Coo" like a dove or a pigeon (or a Scot saying "cow"). They can run at up to 42 kilometres per hour, which is very fast for such a small bird, but hardly fast enough to outrun a coyote that can sprint at 65 kilometres per hour.

Cuckoo in the sense of "mad" supposedly comes from the maddening repetitiveness of the cuckoo's call.

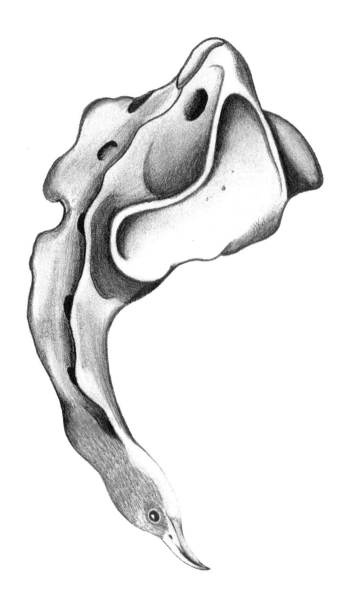

THE COCHLEA

This chapter is the first so far to deal with the inner ear. There will be many more, because anatomists went a bit cuckoo when naming the parts of our hearing apparatus. The inner ear is made of a series of cavities located in the petrous part (literally the "rocky part") of the temporal bone. These cavities include three semi-circular canals, the vestibule and the spiral shaped cochlea. In Latin, a *cochlea* is a "snail shell", and that is exactly what a cast of this cavity would look like.

The pea-sized cochlea contains all the machinery that allows you to detect air-pressure waves, or sound. Sound waves make the eardrum vibrate, and these vibrations are amplified by the ossicles of the middle ear and transferred to the fluid-filled chambers of the cochlea. Hair cells, bearing projections that sway like seaweed on the sea floor, detect the movements of this fluid, and send their information to the brain via the auditory nerve. The brain turns these signals into the sounds we hear, recognise, understand and appreciate. This begs the question, if a tree falls in a forest and there is no cochlea around to turn the pressure waves into a signal that is perceived as sound, does it make a sound? The answer depends on your definition of sound: is it the pressure wave itself, or is it what your brain makes of it?

Cochlear implants are devices that help people with impaired hearing. They consist of a microphone that picks up the sound waves and transmits them to electrodes inside the cochlea. These electrodes stimulate the auditory nerve, which sends the electrical signals to the brain.

To find out more about the machinery of the middle ear and inner ear, see the chapters on the scala, the labyrinth, the malleus and the tympanic membrane. There are so many interesting bits and bobs in the ear that this book could almost have been called "The Ear's Cabinet of Etymological Curiosities".

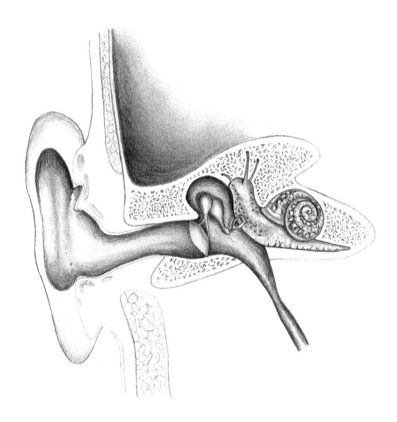

THE CORACOID PROCESS

We have already mentioned cuckoos. Two other chapters will discuss chickens and geese. This chapter is dedicated to crows and ravens. As you can see, the body is full of bird-related terminology.

The coracoid process is a bony protuberance that sticks out of the shoulder blade. You can feel your coracoid process just below your collarbone, at the top of the groove between your shoulder muscle and chest muscle. Coracoid literally means "crow-like", from the Greek word *korax* meaning "crow or raven". Some people think the coracoid process resembles the whole bird, others think it just looks like a crow's beak. In the illustration, the coracoid process is depicted as a crow's head. Funnily enough, ravens do not have coracoid processes, but fully-fledged coracoid bones instead. All birds have large coracoid bones that are essential to flight.

If you happen to dislocate you shoulder on a regular basis, surgeons might kindly offer to saw off your coracoid process and screw it back on somewhere where it will stop the head of the humerus (the arm bone) from leaving its socket. Surgeons sometimes refer to the coracoid process as the "lighthouse of the shoulder" because of its proximity to large blood vessels and nerves and because it is used as a landmark for many shoulder operations. Waggish surgeons have been known to joke that the lateral side of the coracoid is the "safe side", whereas the medial side is the "suicide".

Related words

Corvus corax is the scientific name of the common raven.
Corax is not only a crow, but also a philosopher. Corax of Syracuse was one of the fathers of rhetoric, or "the art of persuasion" as he called it. He has become famous for his court case against Tisias, one of his students who refused to pay his tuition fee for his course on the art of persuasion. Corax argued that if Tisias lost the case, he would have to pay by order of the court, and that even if Tisias won the case he should pay anyway, because it would prove the worth of his course. Tisias responded that if he won the case, he should not pay, and even if he lost the case, he would not have to pay because it would be proof that Corax's instruction was worthless. The judges and bystanders are said to have uttered cries of "Mali corvi, malum ovum", meaning "Bad crow, bad egg".

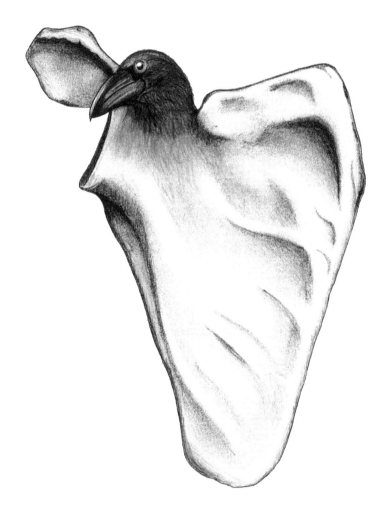

THE COCCYGEAL CORNUA

Who would have thought that cuckoos had horns? The coccygeal cornua, from the Latin *cornu* meaning "horn", are bony projections at the top of the coccyx. Coccyx, as we have already noted in a previous chapter, comes from the Greek for "cuckoo", *kokkux*. The coccygeal cornua articulate with the sacral cornua, two bony projections at the apex (the bottom) of the sacrum. Several other structures in the body come equipped with cornua or horns: the hyoid bone, the lateral ventricles of the brain, the hippocampus, the spinal cord, the uterus and the sacrum. In each hippocampus for instance, we have a *cornu ammonis* (literally "Ammon's Horn") that gained its name because a cross-section of the hippocampus reveals a C-shaped structure that is reminiscent of a ram's horns. Ammon of course is an Egyptian god with the head of a ram.

The hyoid bone is a U-shaped bone in the neck. *Hyoid* literally means "shaped like an upsilon", the Greek letter -u. It is a bone that is well known by those who watch crime dramas, since hyoid bone fractures are often caused by strangulation. The hyoid bone is the only free-floating bone in the human body, meaning that it does not articulate with any other bone. The hyoid has four horns or cornua, two greater and two lesser.

Several newspapers have published clickbait headlines in recent years claiming that teenagers are starting to grow horns on the back of their heads due to excessive smartphone use. However, the paper that inspired these articles (Shahar and Sayers, 2018) was hardly so positive in its conclusions: "We hypothesize EEOP [which stands for Enlarged External Occipital Protuberance – so no mention of horns] may be linked to sustained aberrant postures associated with the emergence and extensive use of hand-held contemporary technologies, such as smartphones and tablets". The media extrapolated these findings so much that the authors were obliged to publish a correction to their original article, removing any references to smartphones.

Related words

A **cornucopia** is a copious *cornu*, a "horn of plenty".
Cornwall is a horn of land or peninsula.
"**Horny**" in the sexual sense probably comes from "having the horn", an old way of expressing male sexual arousal.

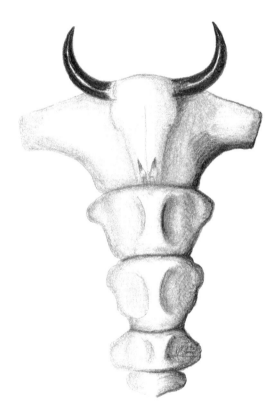

THE CORONOID PROCESS

There are a great many bony projections called "processes" throughout the body. We have already mentioned the crow-shaped *coracoid* process. The *coronoid* process gets its name from the Latin "corona" meaning "crown". There are several crown-related words in anatomy, including two different coronoid processes. The one in the illustration is on the mandible (the lower jawbone). There is another in the elbow, at the top of the ulna. There is also a coronoid fossa of the humerus that receives the coronoid process of the ulna when you bend your elbow. They are not called coronoid because they really look like a crown, but rather because they resemble one of the spikes of a crown.

The coronary arteries are blood vessels that circle the heart like a crown and supply it with blood. People with coronary heart disease have blocked coronary arteries. Coronary stents are little mesh tubes that keep the blocked arteries open so that blood can continue to circulate.

The coronary suture is where the frontal and parietal bones of the skull meet. Oddly enough, the coronary suture does not circle the head as a crown does, but arches over the head like a pair of headphones. Perhaps anatomists were reminded of the laurel wreath, or *corona triumphalis* as it was known in Latin, that, if worn obliquely, vaguely follows the coronary suture.

Related words

A **coroner** is an officer of the crown who investigates deaths.
The **corona** is the outermost part of a star's atmosphere. It is an aura of plasma that extends for millions of kilometres into space. The sun's corona is visible with a special piece of equipment called a coronagraph. If you do not own a coronagraph and wish to see the sun's corona, you will have to wait until the next solar eclipse, which will give you a perfect view of the corona with the naked eye. Well, not completely naked, you should clothe your eye in solar viewing glasses or a very dark pair of welding goggles so as not to suffer retinal burns.
As most people now know, **coronaviruses** have a fringe of projections on their surface, making them look like a crown. Coronaviruses can cause harmless illnesses like the common cold, and very virulent and more life-threatening diseases like Covid 19.
Coronaphobia is the fear of the SARS-CoV-2 virus in particular.

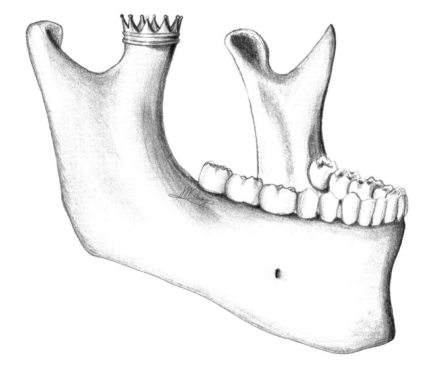

The Cortex

Many organs in the human body have a *cortex*, an outer layer that has a different structure to the inner layers. *Cortex* is the Latin word for "the bark of a tree".

The most famous cortex is probably that of the brain, the cerebral cortex. The cerebral cortex, or grey matter, is made from the cell bodies of neurons. The white matter that lies beneath the cortex is made of axons, which are like long neuronal tails. Axons are like electric cables that transmit nerve impulses (or "action potentials" as they are formally known) from one neuron to another.

Bones also have a cortex, which is a layer of very hard, very dense compact bone. This compact bone, or *cortical* bone, forms a protective casing around the bone marrow and spongy trabecular bone that lies within. The illustration shows the cortical bone of the femur (the thighbone) as the bark of a tree.

Our hairs have a cortex as well. It is the layer of a strand of hair in which melanin is found, the pigment that gives our hair its colour. People with dark hair have a lot of melanin in their cortices, whereas people with blond hair have very little, and people with albinism have practically none at all. There are several types of melanin, including eumelanin and pheomelanin. Redheaded people have a lot of pheomelanin, whereas dark-haired people have a lot of eumelanin.

Most cells have a cellular cortex, a complex network of proteins that lies just below the cell membrane. Amongst other things, these proteins give cells their structure and allow them to change shape when they need to (during cell division for instance).

There are yet more cortices throughout the human body: you might have heard of the renal cortex, the adrenal cortex, the thymic cortex and the ovarian cortex.

Related words

To **decorticate** a tree is to remove its bark. Cork trees get decorticated every few years for instance.

Corticosteroids are hormones that are produced by the adrenal cortex. They are also produced synthetically and used as anti-inflammatory drugs. Unfortunately, they have a very long list of adverse side effects.

THE CRICOID CARTILAGE

The cricoid cartilage is a ring of cartilage that encircles the windpipe (or trachea) and that you can feel just below your Adam's apple. Galen gave it the name "cricoid" because it resembles a signet ring, and the Greek word for a finger ring is *krikos*. The illustration shows a posterior view of the cricoid cartilage and trachea, so that the larger part of the ring that bears the seal is visible. The illustration is incomplete however because the *arytenoid* cartilages (literally "jug-shaped" or "ladle-shaped" cartilages) have been removed. They sit on top of the cricoid cartilage and serve as anchors for the vocal chords.

The trachea is enclosed in many c-shaped cartilaginous rings, but the cricoid cartilage is the only ring that goes all the way around the trachea. The tracheal rings allow the windpipe to be flexible yet strong, a bit like corrugated tubing used by electricians.

There are other rings in the human body, but with different etymological origins: the Latin word for ring is *anus*. The fingers contain ring-shaped *anular* ligaments that act as pulleys for tendons to slide through. The fourth finger, or ring finger, is also known as the *digitus annularis. The* anus needs no introduction.

The elbow also contains an anular ligament that wraps around the head of the radius and keeps it in contact with the ulna (the radius and ulna being the two bones of the forearm). This anular ligament is involved in quite a common injury called "nursemaid's elbow" that usually occurs in toddlers, and results from the radial head slipping out of the grip of the anular ligament. The official name of the injury is "radial head dislocation". This can happen when children are swung around by their arms for instance, or when their arms are forcefully pulled through the sleeve of a tight fitting coat, or when their arms are tugged upon in order to make the lazy rascals walk faster.

Related words

A circle is a ring-shaped geometrical figure.
A circus is a round, ring-shaped arena.
The verb "to search" comes from the French "chercher" which in turn derives from the Latin *circare*, which ultimately comes from the Greek word *krikos*.

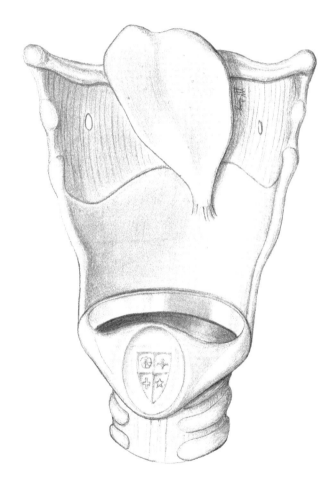

THE CRISTA GALLI

We have already mentioned the avian origins of the coccyx and the coracoid process. The *crista galli* is a third ornithological reference in the anatomical nomenclature. The crista galli is a bony crest that sits atop the ethmoid bone, the bone that separates the nasal cavity from the brain. In Latin, *crista galli* literally means a "cockscomb", the flappy, fleshy growth on top of a chicken's head.

Whereas a chicken's cockscomb is mainly used as an ornament to attract members of the opposite sex, ours is an anchor for the *falx cerebri*, the structure that separates the brain into two hemispheres. Fortunately our cockscombs are hidden away inside our skulls, otherwise who knows what effect it would have on passing birds. Our crista galli also serves to give us headaches occasionally, since something called crista galli pneumatisation has been identified as one of the many possible causes of head pain. In this condition, air somehow manages to find its way into the crista galli from the adjacent ethmoidal and frontal sinuses, and causes pain for some reason.

Cockscombs are only one of the many fleshy growths sported by the birds of the Galliforme family. The galliformes include chickens, partridges, pheasants, turkeys and quails. These birds not only have wobbly growths on their heads, but also have fleshy and colourful earlobes, snoods on their beaks and wattles on their throats. Together, the comb, snood, earlobes and wattle are known as caruncles. Some dinosaurs are thought to have had caruncles that they would use in colourful displays to attract a mate.

Related words

The symbol of France is a cock. It is interesting and somewhat ironic that this symbol was originally a play on words: *gallus* means a cock, but also an inhabitant of Gaul. Little did they anticipate the plays on words that would result from the English translation of this Latin pun.

A **crease** is a **crest** in a garment or fabric for example. Both words come from the Latin *crista*.

Creste di gallo is a shape of pasta that looks like a cockscomb.

Several species of plants are known as cockscomb, either because of their colour or their shape (or both), such as celosia, yellow rattle and *erythrina crista galli*.

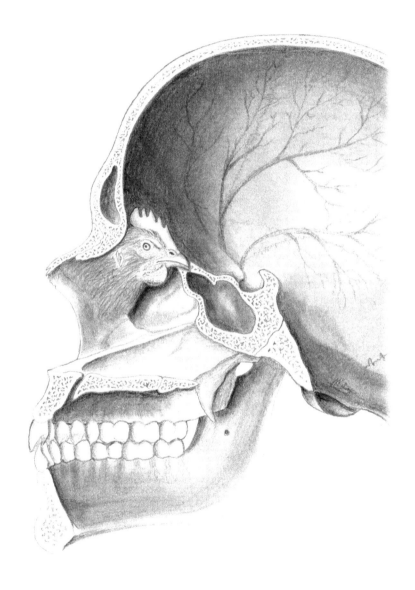

THE ETHMOID BONE

If the sacrum is the holiest bone in the body in the religious sense of the word, the ethmoid is the holiest in terms of perforations. The word "ethmoid" comes from the Greek word *ethmos*, meaning "a sieve". The ethmoid bone separates the left nasal cavity from the right, and both nasal cavities from the brain. It is a fascinating bone that has several interesting features with curious names. The first, the crista galli, is one that we have already discussed in the previous chapter. It is a small bony crest that looks like a cockscomb onto which the falx cerebri attaches, that is to say the membrane that separates the right and left hemispheres of the brain.

The second feature of the ethmoid bone is the ethmoidal labyrinth, a series of air-filled cells that open up into the nasal cavities. The air we breathe whirls around these cells where it is warmed up, filtered and moistened in order to protect our lungs and airways.

The third feature of the ethmoid bone is the cribriform plate, a thin layer of bone that lies either side of the crista galli and separates the brain from the nasal cavity. The separation is not completely impermeable though, because the cribriform plate is riddled with very small holes for olfactory nerve fibres to enter the nose, allowing us to detect smells. Just as the ethmoid bone got its name from the Greek word for sieve, the cribriform plate got its name from the Latin equivalent, *cribrium*. This is where we get the adjective "cribbled", used to describe something that has a pattern of small holes or dots. The holes of the cribriform plate can sometimes close up with age, leading to a decreased sense of smell. Sometimes, accidents can cause cerebrospinal fluid, the watery substance in which the central nervous system bathes, to leak out of through the cribriform plate. This condition is called rhinorrhoea, a word that shares its origins with "diarrhoea" (*rhein* meaning "to flow" in Greek). Luckily that is where the connection ends. Diarrhoea pouring out of the nostrils is not a thought to be dwelt upon.

The handle of the sieve in the illustration represents the thin wall of bone that separates the left and right nasal cavities, called the nasal septum (*septum* meaning "hedge, fence or barrier" in Latin). The top of the septum is made of the perpendicular plate of the ethmoid bone, whereas the bottom half is made by the vomer bone. *Vomer* means "ploughshare" in Latin, and the vomer bone does indeed bear a striking resemblance to the blade of a plough.

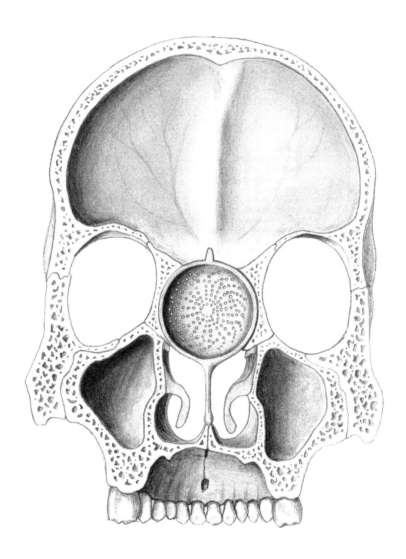

THE FABELLA

The fabella is what is called an "accessory" bone or "supernumerary" bone, *i.e.* a bone that some people have and others do not. Other accessory bones include the cyamella (also in the knee), the os peroneum (in the ankle) and the os trigonum (in the heel) among many others. Very often, accessory bones are also sesamoid bones (that we shall talk about in another chapter).

Fabella is the diminutive of the Latin word *faba* meaning "bean", so the fabella is the "little bean". This is also where we get our word "fava bean" from, which is a synonym of broad bean. The fabella is present in about one third of people, and is located in the tendon of the lateral gastrocnemius (a calf muscle), on the outside of the back of the knee. It is usually between half a centimetre and two centimetres in diameter.

The fabella is usually completely harmless, but sometimes it is thought to cause conditions such as fabella pain syndrome, common fibular nerve palsy and popliteal artery entrapment syndrome. Several other supernumerary bones can cause similar painful conditions. Os trigonum syndrome is pain at the back of the ankle when you point your toes due to a small bone that gets wedged between the calcaneus (the heel bone) and the back of the tibia (the shinbone). Painful os peroneum syndrome is pain on the side of the foot that can be due to a fractured os peroneum or a tear in the tendon that the os peroneum sits in (the fibularis longus tendon).

Beans are a particularly good source of protein, fibre, vitamin B9 and iron. They also contain complex sugars called oligosaccharides, which are not well digested by our human enzymes, but are better taken care of by the bacteria in our colon. When bacteria break down these oligosaccharides, they produce methane and other gases that we noisily release as flatulence.

Beans are not only toxic because they make us release malodorous clouds of gas. Some beans, such as kidney beans, contain a toxin called phytohaemagglutinin that must be destroyed by cooking before the beans are consumed. The word "phytohaemagglutinin" comes from *phyto* meaning "plant", *haem* meaning "blood", *agglut* meaning "to agglutinate", and the suffix "–in" used for proteins. So phytohaemagglutinin is literally a protein from a plant that agglutinates blood cells. Common symptoms of bean poisoning are nausea, vomiting and diarrhoea.

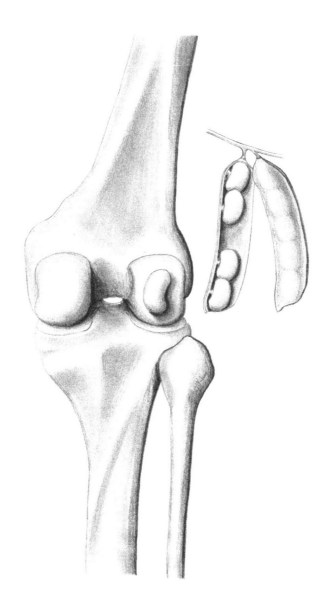

THE FALX CEREBRI

Our brains, like the Earth, are divided into two hemispheres. These hemispheres are separated not horizontally by an equator, but vertically by a structure called the *falx cerebri*. Viewed from the side, it looks like a sickle has sliced the brain in two and become lodged in the head. *Falx cerebri* is Latin for "the sickle of the brain".

The falx cerebri is actually a fold of dura mater (literally "tough mother"), one of the three membranes that envelop the brain. The tip of the blade of the falx cerebri attaches to the crista galli, a little crest of bone that resembles a cockscomb. The other end of the falx cerebri attaches to the top of the tentorium cerebelli (literally "the tent of the cerebellum"), a tent-like sheet of connective tissue that separates the cerebrum, "the brain", from the cerebellum, "the little brain".

There are other sickle-shaped things in the body that share the same etymology. There is a falciform ligament for instance, that attaches the liver to the anterior wall of the abdomen and separates the liver into two lobes. Some people also have a hepatic falciform artery in their liver. People with sickle-cell disease are said to have falciform red blood cells, and the disease in known in many languages as "falciform anaemia".

Related words

A **falcon** is a bird of prey with a beak that is curved like the blade of a scythe or sickle.
The adjective "**falcate**" means sickle shaped, curved like a scythe or sickle. A falcon's beak can be described as falcate.
Defalcation is the act of cutting off or deducting a part, as you might with a sickle.
A **falchion** is a type of broadsword with a curved blade, like the beak of a falcon or the blade of a scythe.

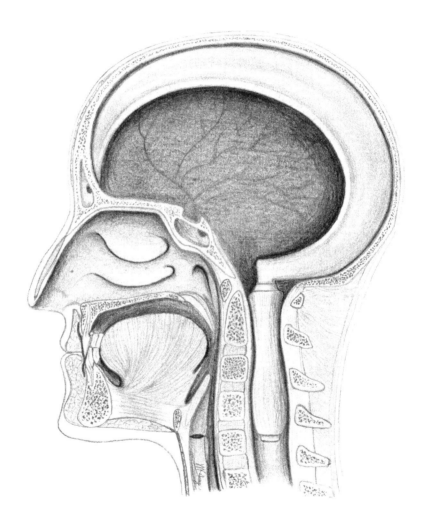

Fascia

Fascia is probably one of the most extensive and important body parts that most people have never heard of. It is a network of fibrous connective tissue (the same stuff that ligaments and tendons are made of) that wraps around every single bone, every single muscle, and every single organ. It both unites and separates adjacent organs. The Latin word *fascia* means a "band or bandage".

The fascial system was overlooked for a long time because it was treated as an inert substance that simply supported the other more important organs. The fascia was seen by anatomists as something to cut away as quickly as possible to get to the more interesting organs hidden beneath. Recently however, researchers have become more interested in this tissue, and have discovered that it harbours a rich vascular and nervous supply. Fascia has since started to be investigated as a possible source of mysteriously painful conditions like low back pain.

The fascia represented in the illustration is the fascia lata (*lata* means "broad" in Latin), a thick layer of connective tissue that envelops the thigh. If you are a runner, you will probably have heard of the iliotibial band, a thickening of the fascia lata that is notorious for its involvement in iliotibial band friction syndrome, a common condition amongst runners.

There are at least two other bandages in the human body, the *splenius capitis* ("the bandage of the head") and the *splenius cervicis* ("the bandage of the neck"), two neck muscles that allow you to turn your head and tilt your head upwards.

Related words

In anatomy, a **fascicle** or **fasciculus** is a bundle of fibres surrounded by connective tissue.
In sociology, a **fascist** group is a bundle of violent racist ultranationalists.
In physiotherapy, fascia therapy, or **myofascial** therapy, is basically a massage that aims to decrease myofascial pain, *i.e.* mysterious pain in the muscle or fascia with no reliably identified cause. Foam rollers and stretching are types of fascia therapy.
In carpentry, the **fascia board** around a roof is a band of wood that hides the ends of the rafters.

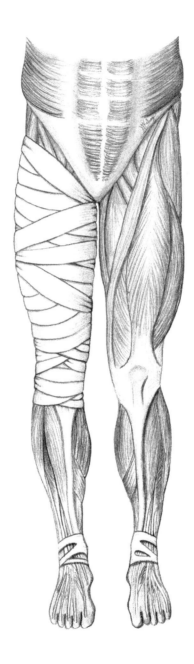

THE FIBULA

The fibula is the thin bone that runs along the outside of the shin bone, or tibia. You can feel the head of the fibula on the outside of your knee, at the end of the easily located tendon of the biceps femoris muscle (*i.e.* the outer hamstring). The other end of the fibula is the bony lump on the outside of your ankle, known as the lateral malleolus.

Fibula is Latin for "brooch, clasp or pin". Fibulae were very common objects because they were used by the Romans to keep their togas from falling off. The Roman fibulae that are sometimes found by archaeologists and metal detectorists very much resemble modern day safety pins. The fibula bone was given its name because it is finer and pointier than the tibia, and looks somewhat needle-like. The resemblance to a pin is far more striking in birds. The very sharp pointy bone in a chicken drumstick is the fibula.

The fibula is often involved in athletic injuries. Athletes, especially endurance runners, are prone to stress fractures. Usually, fractures are caused by a single traumatic event (a fall, an accident, etc.). Stress fractures on the other hand appear over time as a result of excessive repetitive stress and overuse. Stress fractures of the fibula are known as "runner's fractures". Most ankle sprains involve a ligament that stretches from the tip of the fibula to the talus called the anterior talofibular ligament. In particularly bad sprains, the ligament can tear (or "avulse") a piece of bone from the lateral malleolus of the fibula.

Several other structures in the leg contain the word "fibula" because of their proximity to the bone: the common fibular nerve, the fibular artery, and three fibularis muscles (longus, brevis and tertius). To contract your fibularis muscles, try walking on the inner side of your feet whilst lifting the outer side.

All of these structures have another, synonymous name: the *peroneal* nerve, artery and muscles. "Peroneal" derives from the Greek word *perone*, which is the Greek equivalent of the Latin word *fibula*.

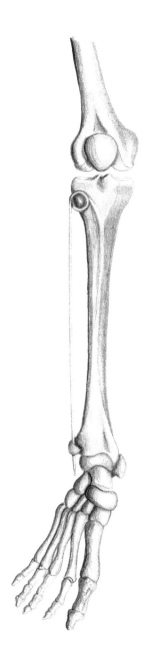

FONTANELLES

If you have ever touched the skull of a new born baby, you will know that it is very unlike the (both literally and figuratively) rock-hard, almost impenetrable skull of an adult. Infants' skulls have soft spots, officially known as *fontanelles*. The word *fontanelle* is an old French word meaning "little fountain" which itself comes from the Latin word *fontana* meaning "spring". Perhaps it got its name from the fact that if the fontanelle is damaged, cerebrospinal fluid can leak out of the head like water from a fountain or a spring. Cerebrospinal fluid is a clear, water-like fluid in which the brain and the rest of the central nervous system bathe. Others think that soft spots might have been called fontanelles because they resemble the little depression or dent in the ground that usually surrounds a natural spring.

There are two fontanelles, one anterior and one posterior. The latter closes rather quickly, between one and two months after birth, whereas the former takes a little longer (between 9 and 18 months). The fontanelles help the skull to stay supple, allowing the brain to grow and develop. A supple skull also helps during childbirth, when a flexible head is a snazzy feature to have for a baby, since it provides a certain degree of pain relief both for the mother and for the baby.

Babies' fontanelles provide a once in a lifetime chance to view the brain using ultrasound imaging. Once the fontanelles have closed, ultrasound waves just bounce off the skull and are completely unable to penetrate it, making it impossible to examine the brain using this technique.

It is a good idea to keep an eye on the fontanelles, because they can bulge out if intracranial pressure is too high, or sink in in case of dehydration.

Related words

A **font** is a basin of water used during baptisms.
A **fount** of knowledge is a source of knowledge.
A **fountain pen** is literally a feather with its own spring of ink. As mentioned elsewhere, the word "pen" comes from *pinna*, meaning "feather", because quills were made of feathers.

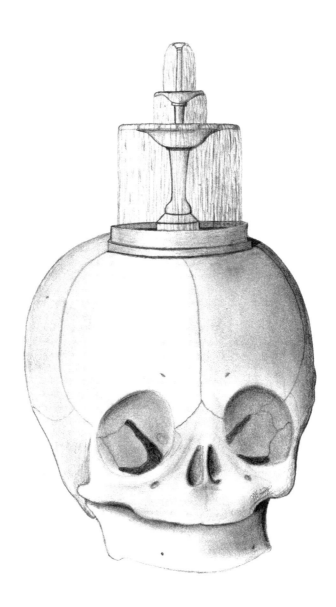

THE GLANS PENIS

The "acorn" would be both a more poetic and more etymologically appropriate name for the structure commonly known as the bell-end. The structure at the tip of the penis is technically called the *glans penis*, from the Latin *glans*, meaning "acorn". In fact, all glands in the body share the same origin. When anatomists named the pineal gland, they obviously had a hard time deciding whether it was a pine nut or an acorn.

Woman too have a *glans* at the end of the clitoris. The glans of the clitoris is actually what most people believe to be the entire organ. In fact, the clitoris is a wishbone-shaped erectile structure that can reach more than 10 cm in length and extends into the vaginal walls.

If you believe in God, penis design was his strong point. If you accept the theory of evolution, some penises are considered examples of so called "runaway sexual selection", where things just get bigger and better and weirder over the generations. In any case, the huge variety of penis designs just goes to show that you cannot use the same tool for every job. Most of us are familiar with the human penis, but other animals sometimes have much more interesting appendages. Here are some examples:

- The glans penis of the cat is covered in penile spines (little thorn-like growths), and their penis itself contains a vestigial bone.

- The Argentine lake duck is famous for being the vertebrate with the longest penis in relation to its size: about 43 centimetres, or 17 inches.

- The barnacle is the overall winner, with a penis forty times its size.

- Snakes famously have a forked tongue, but they also have a forked, Y-shaped penis made of two hooked hemipenises that prevent the female from slithering away during coitus.

- The Argonaut octopus has a detachable penis that swims away on its own to inseminate the female, which is several times the size of the male. After releasing its penis, the male dies.

- Orb-weaver spiders also have detachable penises that break off during mating so that the male can slip away before being eaten.

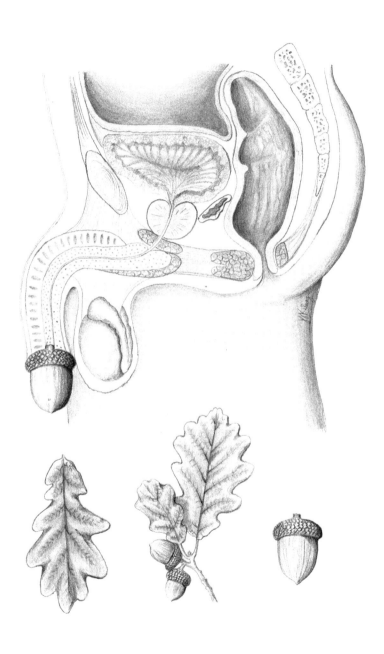

THE HAMATE BONE

The carpal bones are the bones of the wrist, not the bones of the fresh-water fish. There are eight carpal bones in each wrist, several of which have their own chapter in this book. The carpal bones are roughly organised into two rows of four. The first row contains the scaphoid, the lunate bone, the triquetrum and the pisiform. The second row is composed of the trapezium, the trapezoid the capitate bone and the hamate bone.

The hamate bone is also known as the unciform bone. "Unciform" and "hamate" come from the Latin words *uncus* and *hamus* respectively, both of which mean "hook". The hamate bone has a bony hook-shaped process called the *hamulus*, the diminutive of *hamus*, meaning "little hook". The hook serves as an anchor for ligaments and tendons.

The hook of the hamate bone is commonly fractured, especially in athletes such as golfers when they hit the ground too hard, hockey players when they hit the ice and baseball players from hitting the ball repetitively. Some baseball players actually have the hook of the hamate removed. It can also be fractured during a Fall On an Out-Stretched Hand, an accident so common it has become known as a FOOSH.

There are several other hooks throughout the body: there is an uncus in the brain (a roughly hook-shaped structure in the parahippocampal gyrus), and there are uncinate processes on the ethmoid bone, on some vertebrae and in the pancreas as well.

Related words

The barbs on the wings of insects are known as **hamuli**, and so are the little hooks that allow the barbs of a bird's feather to stick together like Velcro®.
The names of plants that have hook-like features often contain the word "uncus": *uncaria* and *uncinatum* are both hook-bearing plants for example.

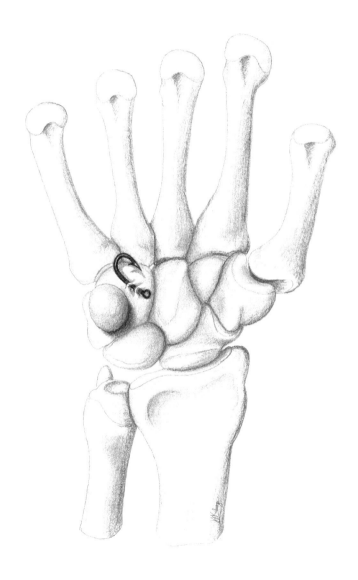

THE HIPPOCAMPUS

The hippocampus is a structure deep inside the brain that is involved primarily in memory formation, particularly spatial memory. London taxi drivers, who have excellent spatial memory because they need to know the streets of London like the back of their hand, have very large hippocampi. On the other hand, depressed and stressed people tend to have smaller hippocampi. The structure was named for its shape: *hippocampus* means seahorse in Latin (from the Greek *hippo* meaning "horse", and *kampus* meaning "sea monster").

As we have already discussed in the chapter concerning the amygdala, people with bits of their brain missing have been crucial in understanding the role of different brain structures in cognition. Patient HM is probably the best-known patient in the history of neuroscience, and perhaps medicine. His full name is Henry Molaison. In 1953, he had both of his hippocampi and a few other important bits and pieces removed from his brain in order to cure him from a very serious form of epilepsy. The treatment was pretty successful, but it left him with a complete inability to form new memories, a condition known as anterograde amnesia. However, there are different types of memory, and not all were affected. Even if you spent all day with him today, he would be unable to recall your name tomorrow. However, if he spent all day learning a new motor skill today, although tomorrow he would not remember having learned the skill, he would still be able to perform it.

One of the tasks that H. M. had to learn, and is commonly used in neuroscience experiments, is fun to do at home with minimal equipment. It involves tracing the outline of a star without looking directly at your hand, but by looking in a mirror instead. It is a lot harder than it sounds. Have a look on the internet for more detailed instructions.

Related words

A **hippopotamus** is a "river horse".

A **hippodrome** is a horse's race course.

A **hippogriff** is the offspring of a horse and a griffin. Hippogriffs have the front half of an eagle and the back half of a horse, whereas griffins have an eagle's head and wings on a lion's body.

Hippopotomonstrosesquippedaliophobia is the fear of very long, hippo-sized words. People with this phobia are of course unable to name their condition.

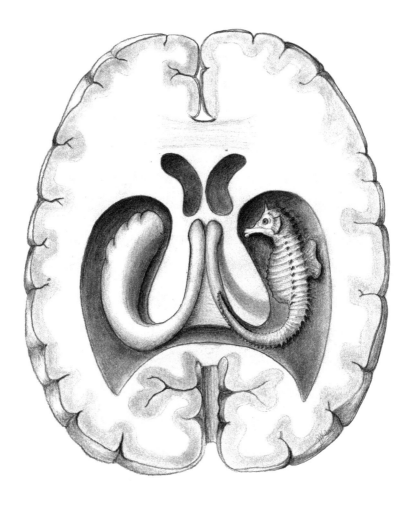

THE INDEX

We have five digits on each hand, each of which has been given a Latin name that we rarely use in everyday life, one exception being the index finger. Index comes from the Latin *indicare*, meaning "to indicate, to point out", because it is the finger that we point with.

The thumb is technically known as the pollex, which comes from the Latin *pollere*, meaning "strong", because it is the brawniest of the five digits.

They obviously lacked inspiration when they named the *digitus medius*, which literally means the "middle finger". It used to have a better name though: *digitus impudicus*, meaning the "shameless or offensive finger".

The fourth finger is known as the *annularis*, meaning the "ring finger". But why do we associate the fourth finger with love? It was once thought that a *vena amoris*, or "vein of love", travelled directly from the fourth finger to the heart. Another name for the ring finger is the *digitus medicinalis*, which may come from the practice of using this finger to apply medical ointments.

The pinkie can be called the *digitus minimus* ("little finger") or, more interestingly, the *auricularis* because it fits nicely into the auditory canal and can be used as an ear bud for removing excess earwax. *Auricularis* comes from the diminutive of *auris* meaning "ear".

The act of finger counting is technically known as dactylonomy. Today we mainly use the decimal system for counting and calculating, and so quite naturally we learn to count to ten on the ten fingers of our hands. It is no coincidence that we use the same word, "digit", to refer to the fingers and to the numbers 0 to 9. However, it is possible to count much higher using your ten fingers alone. If you count the three phalanges of each finger using the thumb as a pointer, you can count to 12 on one hand. You could also count how many times you reach twelve on the opposite hand, using the same system. Thus, you can count to 144. If you count the creases between the phalanges as well, you can count to 24 on one hand and 576 using both. The ultimate way of counting using your fingers is called "finger binary", where each successive finger represents a higher power of two. The left thumb is 2^0, the left index is 2^1, the left middle finger is 2^2, and so on until you reach the right thumb, 2^{10}. Thus, if you raise the pinkie on the left hand, you are counting 2^4, or 16. If you raise the 1st, 3rd and 4th fingers on the left hand, you are counting $2^0 + 2^2 + 2^3 = 1 + 4 + 8 = 13$. If you raise all ten fingers, you can count to 1023.

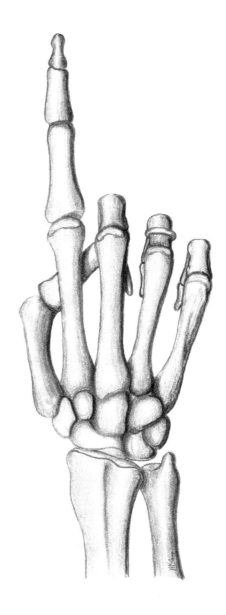

THE IRIS

Iris was the Greek goddess of rainbows. She was also a messenger of the Gods, and she would create rainbows as she carried messages from Mount Olympus to the Earth.

The word *iris* came to be used by the Greeks to describe any brightly coloured circle such as the round, colourful patterns on a peacock's tail, and of course the colourful part of the eye that surrounds the pupil.

The iris is actually made of two doughnut shaped muscles, one that constricts and one that dilates the pupil. The colour of the iris is determined by the amount of melanin it contains. Although human irises never take on all the colours of the rainbow at once, as shown in the illustration, they can be brown, blue, green, grey, hazel, violet, or even pink (in albinos). Human eyes can also appear red, but only in photographs and under the right lighting conditions. This phenomenon is called "red eye" and results from light reflecting off the back of the eye when the pupils are dilated. Some people have two different coloured irises, a condition known as *heterochromia*. Huskies are famous for having heterochromatic eyes.

The plants called irises are thought to have got their name because of the wide variety of colours that flowers of the iris species can have.

Related words

Something **iridescent** displays the colours of the rainbow, like oil on a puddle of water.
Iridium is a heavy metallic element. For the pub quiz aficionados reading this, remember that Ir is the chemical symbol of iridium, not iron. The chemical symbol for iron is Fe, from the Latin *ferrum*, that has given us words like ferrous, ferric and ferritin.
The adjective **iridian** combines all three meanings: it can be applied to anything related to the iris of the eye, anything resembling a rainbow, and anything containing iridium.
Iridiology is a branch of alternative medicine based on the belief that the characteristics of the iris, such as colour and patterns, can give information on a patient's general health.
In modern Greek, a rainbow is an "iridia", or an "ouranio toxo", meaning Uranus's arch. Uranus was the first Greek god of the sky.

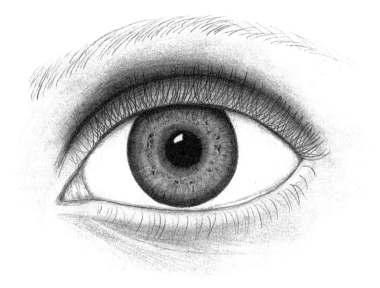

THE GLENOID LABRUM

When you hear the word "lips", you tend to think of the red things around the rim of the mouth. However, there are several other lips in the human body.

A *labrum* is a ring of cartilage that sits around the socket of some ball and socket joints, like the shoulder and hip for instance. These lips of cartilage make the socket deeper, helping to keep the ball in place and stabilising the joint. The illustration shows the labrum around the glenoid fossa of the scapula, that is to say the lip around the socket where the humeral head fits into the shoulder blade. The word "glenoid" comes from the Greek *glene*, meaning "mirror". Perhaps this is because the glenoid fossa is covered in glistening cartilage that gleams like a mirror. Tears of the glenoid labrum, known as SLAP lesions, are common athletic injuries that occur mainly in throwers (javelin throwers, baseball players, handball players, etc.).

Women have two additional pairs of lips: the labia minora and the labia majora, which form part of the vulva, the visible female genitalia. The labia are a surprisingly common source of discontent among women who strive to meet cultural ideals. Labiasplasty is a surgical procedure that is usually intended to shorten a woman's labia minora, whereas labia stretching is the elongation of the labia minora for extended periods of time in order to enlarge them.

The lips around our mouths are a pinkish red colour for two reasons. First, the skin of the lips is thinner than in most places, and so the red blood in the superficial blood vessels is more visible. Second, the skin of the lips is devoid of melanin, the brown pigment that colours the rest of our skin, and so there is nothing to mask the red of the underlying capillaries. Incidentally, the word "capillary" comes from the Latin word for hair, *capillus*, because of the hair-like fineness of these tiny blood vessels.

Other features of the lips include their lack of hair, their thin *stratum corneum* (the outer layer of hard skin, the lack of which makes your lips softer than most other areas of skin), their wealth of sensory nerve endings (which makes your lips perfect for testing the temperature of food and for kissing) and their lack of sebaceous glands (glands that secrete sebum, a substance that moisturises the skin).

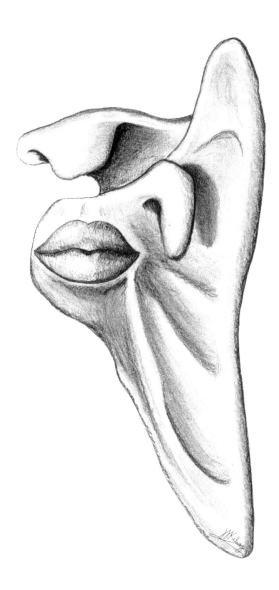

THE LABYRINTH

As mentioned elsewhere, the temporal bone has quite a complicated shape. The outside of the bone has several visible features such as the mastoid process and the zygomatic process, whereas the inside contains a maze of tunnels and cavities called the bony labyrinth. A labyrinth is of course another word for a maze, from the Greek *laburinthos* (whereas "maze" shares the same root as "amaze", from the Middle English word *masen*, meaning "to perplex, bewilder, confound").

The labyrinth in Greek mythology was an underground maze created by the architect Daedalus on the island of Crete. The labyrinth housed the Minotaur, a monster with the body of a man and the head and tail of a bull.

Fortunately, the labyrinth of the human inner ear does not house a Minotaur, but does enclose a snail-shell shaped cavity called the *cochlea,* a chamber called the vestibule, and three semi-circular canals. The cochlea contains the organ of hearing, whereas the vestibule and semi-circular canals contain structures involved in balance.

The vestibule, which is an architectural term meaning a kind of antichamber, houses two little pouches, the saccule and the utricle. These pouches contain crystals called otoliths (literally "ear stones") that lie on a carpet of sensory hair cells. These crystals move around according to the position of your head and pull on the underlying sensory hair cells that send this information to the brain. The cells in the utricle detect vertical movements whereas those in the saccule detect horizontal movements.

The three semi-circular canals on the other hand detect movements like head tilting, head shaking and nodding. In a rather common condition called "benign paroxysmal positional vertigo", or BPPV for short, some of the crystals of the utricle become dislodged and fall into one of the semi-circular canals. These crystals brush up against the sensory cells at the end of the canal, and make your brain think that your head is spinning when in fact you are perfectly still. Interestingly, BPPV is diagnosed by looking at the patient's eye movements. Because the brain thinks that the head is spinning, the eyes move accordingly in an attempt to maintain clear vision. This produces jerky eye movements called a "nystagmus", which looks something like the rapid eye movements you can see in someone gazing into the middle distance in a moving vehicle.

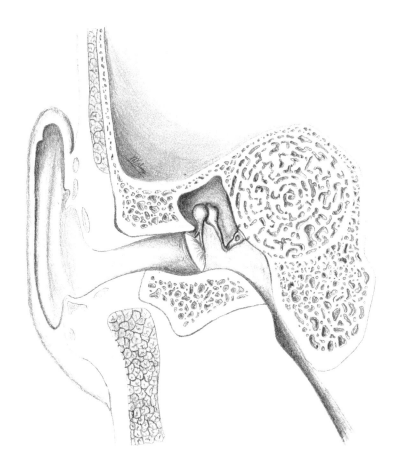

THE LACERTUS FIBROSUS

The biceps stretches from the shoulder blade to the radius, one of the two bones of the forearm. The lacertus fibrosus, also known as the bicipital aponeurosis, is a kind of offshoot that branches off from the thick bicipital tendon that helps to tether the far end of the biceps to the forearm.

Literally, the *lacertus fibrosus* means the "fibrous lizard", perhaps because it curls around the inside of the forearm and resembles the flexible tail of a lizard curling around the branch of a tree.

Sometimes, both the thick biceps tendon and the lacertus fibrosus can snap, allowing the biceps muscle to migrate upwards towards the shoulder. This creates a very short, bulging muscle clinically known as Popeye's sign. Most of the time, when this tendon snaps, it needs to be surgically reattached. For a long time, surgeons would not bother repairing the lacertus fibrosus, perhaps hoping it would grow back like the tail of a lizard. More recently however, surgeons have begun repairing both the tendon and the lacertus fibrosus, thus improving recovery and strength. Sometimes, the biceps tendon breaks but the lacertus fibrosus remains intact. This prevents the biceps from migrating upwards, and can make tendon repair easier.

Lizards can famously self-amputate their tails to escape predators in an act known as autotomy. Some spiders can autotomize their legs, some crabs can autotomize their claws, some starfish can autotomize their legs, and some mice (African spiny mice) can even autotomize their skin.

The word "autotomy" shares the same origin as the word "anatomy": *tomia* means "cutting" in Greek, *ana* means "up" and *auto* means "self". Thus, anatomy means "cutting up" and autotomy means "self-cutting".

Related words

The scientific name of the lizard family is the *lacertidae*, and lizards in that family bear the name *lacerta*, like *lacerta viridis* (the green lizard) and *lacerta agilis* (the sand lizard). Lacerta is also one of the 88 modern constellations described by the International Astronomical Union. Like with most constellations, you need a special kind of imagination to see why a line of faint stars was thought to resemble a lizard.

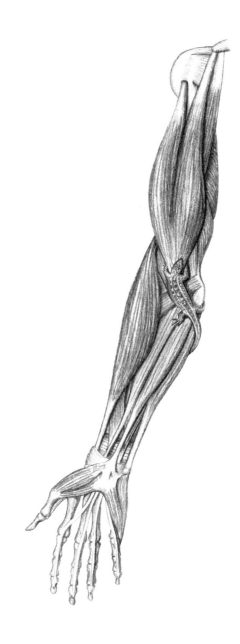

THE LACRIMAL BONE

The lacrimal bone is one of the seven bones that make up the eye socket. It is so thin that if you hold it up to the sun, the light will shine through it. The lacrimal bone gets its name from the fact that it lies beneath the lacrimal sac and houses the lacrimal duct. The word "lacrimal" comes from the Latin word *lacrima*, meaning "tear".

The lacrimal plumbing and drainage system is rather intricate and interesting. Tears are produced by the lacrimal glands, and are conveyed to the surface of the eye by tubes called the excretory lacrimal ducts. You produce them all the time, not only when you are crying (about 1 ml every day in the absence of excess mirth or grief). Blinking spreads the tears over the eyeballs to lubricate them so that they can easily swivel around inside their sockets. Tears also contain antibacterial substances, as does sweat, to stave off infections. Excess tears accumulate in the lacrimal lake, that small pool of tears that you can see in the corner of your eye, before being drained out through little holes called the lacrimal puncta. When you produce too many tears, the puncta cannot deal with the flow, and the lake overflows. This is known as crying, or lacrimation. Most of the time, tears do not travel down the cheek, but down the lacrimal canaliculi and fall into the lacrimal sac, that empties via the nasolacrimal duct into the nose.

Related words

The English word "lachrymose", meaning sad and tearful, shares the same origin but the spelling has evolved differently over time. Both words, lacrimal and lachrymose, come from the Greek word *dakryma*, meaning "tear". The -d is thought to have become an -l through a process known as the "Sabine –L", the Sabines being a people who lived in Italy before the rise of the Roman Empire and who have (probably wrongly) become famous for their mispronunciation of the letter -d. The -d in several Greek and Old Latin words became an -l in more recent Latin: Odysseus became Ulysses, *dingua* became *lingua* ("language"), and *olere* ("to smell") became *odor*. The –ch and –y in lachrymose come from the practice of medieval scholars of replacing –c by –ch, and –i by –y because they thought it looked better.

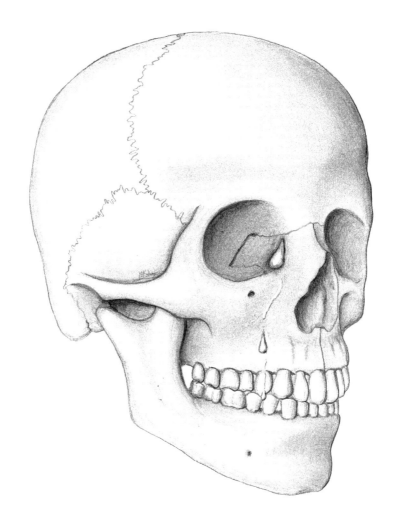

LIGAMENTS

Ligaments are often confused with tendons. Ligaments connect one bone to another, whereas tendons connect muscle to bone. The word "ligament" comes from the Latin *ligare*, which means "to tie, to bind, to attach". The illustration shows some of the many ligaments of the knee joint. The rope is the medial collateral ligament on the inside of the knee, the adjustable strap is the patellofemoral ligament that links the kneecap to the shinbone and the chains are the cruciate ligaments that lie deep within the knee joint.

When you sprain a joint, the ligaments surrounding that joint stretch, tear or completely snap depending on the severity of the sprain. In some cases, surgeons will either repair or replace the snapped ligament using a tendon that they harvest from an unsuspecting muscle somewhere else in the body. They can also use artificial ligaments made from synthetic materials.

Through training, gymnasts not only stretch their muscles but also their ligaments, making them more flexible. For example, doing the front splits requires a particularly elongated iliofemoral ligament. Other people are born with hypermobile joints and are able to move their joints beyond the normal range of motion. Hypermobile people are also known as double-jointed or loose-jointed. Their increased mobility is often due to longer, more stretchy ligaments, but sometimes it is actually the bones that make up the joint that are a slightly different shape to most people's.

Related words

A **ligature** is anything that is used for binding things together.
In linguistics, two letters bound together like "œ" and "æ" are called ligatures.
In chemistry, a **ligand** is a substance that binds to another to form a larger molecule.

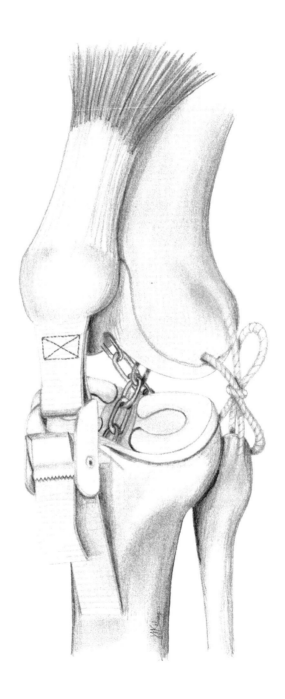

THE LUMBRICAL MUSCLES

As we have already seen, you have seahorses in your brain, a cuckoo at the base of your spine and a lizard in your elbow. You also have worms in your hands. The *lumbrical* muscles are small muscles in the hands that allow you to straighten the fingers and bend the joint between the hand and the fingers, *i.e.* the metacarpophalangeal joint. They are called the lumbrical muscles because they look like little worms (from the Latin *lumbricus* meaning "worm"). The common earthworm is known to biologists as *lumbricus terrestris*, and is considered a pest in many countries where it has recently been introduced and represents competition for local earthworms. "Bloody common earthworms, coming over here, stealing our native earthworms' food..."

The lumbrical muscles can be paralysed when the ulnar nerve is damaged, leading to a condition called ulnar claw, or "spinster's claw". People with this condition are unable to extend the last two fingers (the ring finger and little finger). The ulnar nerve is sometimes called the musician's nerve because it helps to control the fine movements of the fingers.

The great mystery is why this condition is called "spinster's claw". A spinster is a woman who is old enough to be married but is not, and is unlikely ever to get married. In the past, married women often got better jobs than unmarried women. A typical job for an unmarried woman was spinning wool, hence the word "spinster". Maybe spinsters would be ashamed of not having a ring on their finger, and so would bend the fourth and fifth fingers down to hide their ringlessness. Or perhaps ulnar nerve compression was one of the occupational hazards of spinning wool.

For medical students, ulnar claw is often confused with the sign of benediction, which is caused by damage to the median nerve, and prevents you from making a fist because you cannot fold the thumb, index and middle finger. Both signs look very similar, but one is a default position of the hand while the other is only visible when you try to make a fist. Spinster's claw can also be confused with Dupuytren's disease, where the fascia that covers the palm of the hand basically shrinks and pulls the last two fingers down with it.

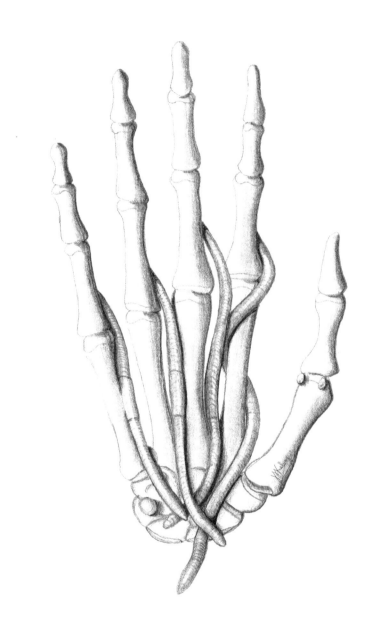

THE LUNATE BONE

As its name suggests, the lunate bone is moon-shaped. It is in fact the shape of a half-moon, and used to be known as the semilunar bone. It is one of the eight small wrist bones known as the carpal bones. The word "lunate" comes from the Latin *luna*, meaning "moon", and *lunatum*, meaning "half-moon shaped".

The lunate bone is the second most fractured bone in the wrist after the scaphoid. Both bones can break as a result of a FOOSH (a fall on an outstretched hand). The lunate bone can also be the victim of a strange disease, called Kienbock's disease, or avascular necrosis, in which the blood supply to the lunate disappears leading to the death of the lunate bone. Many people think of bone as a stony, white, dead substance, because that is what we see when we look at a skeleton. Real live bones however are very much alive. They contain blood vessels, cells and nerve endings. They are continually growing and repairing themselves. Living bones are more of a pinkish colour than white, because of the blood vessels that supply them with oxygen and nutrients.

There is another structure in the human body that is named after its resemblance to the moon. This one is not half-moon shaped, but the shape of a crescent moon. Can you guess what it is? Here is a clue: the Greek word for moon is *mene*.

Related words

The adjective **lunar** means "pertaining to the moon".
A **lunatic** is someone who is insane. It is an old word that was coined due to a belief that some forms of insanity were brought about by changes in the phases of the moon. **Loony** is an abbreviation of lunatic.
Lunatic soup is slang for an alcoholic beverage.
Nowadays, **sublunary** is a poetic way of saying earthly, mundane, but in the past, according to Aristotelian physics, the sublunary sphere was that part of the universe located between the Earth and the moon.
A **lunation** is another word for a lunar month, *i.e.* the period of time averaging 29 days, 12 hours, 44 minutes and 2.8 seconds that elapses between two successive new moons.

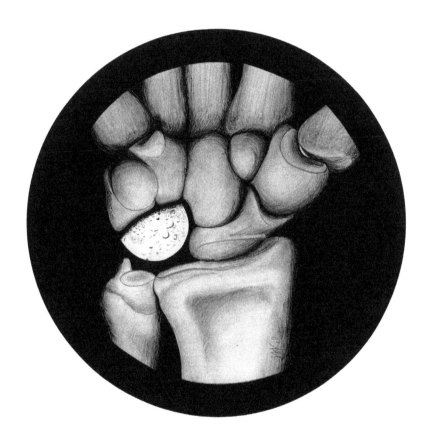

THE MALLEOLI

The knobbly bits of bone on either side of your ankle are known as *malleoli*. The one on the inside of the ankle is the medial malleolus, and the one on the outside is the lateral malleolus. The word *malleolus* is the diminutive of the Latin word for hammer, *malleus*. We also have a *malleus* in each ear, but funnily enough, the "little hammers" of the ankles are about a hundred times larger than the "hammers" of the inner ears. One feels that the diminutive is an unfair one.

The malleoli serve as anchor points for many ligaments that reinforce and stabilise the ankle joint. If you have ever sprained an ankle, you have probably damaged the ligaments that attach to the lateral malleolus. If you sprain your ankle severely enough, the ligaments can pull so hard on the lateral malleolus that bits of bone can be pulled off, resulting in a malleolar fracture. Lateral malleolus fractures are the most common ankle fractures, though luckily they are often treated without surgery.

Related words

Of course, the English word "mallet" comes from the same Latin root. A **maul** is like a mallet, but larger, and also comes from *malleus*. The verb "**to maul**" originally meant to beat with a heavy weapon like a maul. Since then, to maul has come to mean "seriously damage or injure", as in the phrase "mauled by a dog".

The sticks used to strike the keys of a xylophone are called mallets.

Something that is **malleable** is easily deformed or moulded. The word "malleable" was first used for metals that were able to be hammered into shape with a mallet.

Mallow, or *althaea officinalis*, is a purple flower that grows in marshes. The word "mallow" is completely unrelated to the Latin word *malleus*, apart from the fact that the first four letters are the same. But this is a cabinet of curiosities, and unrelated things often end up sharing the same shelf. As you might have guessed, the marsh-mallow plant was once the main ingredient for making marshmallows. The Latin word for mallow is *malva*, which gave us the colour "mauve".

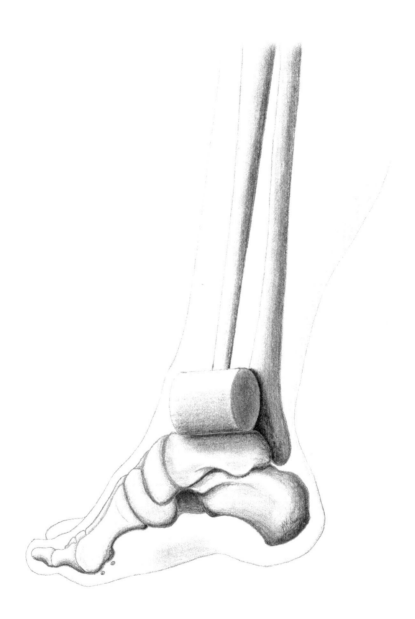

THE MALLEUS

As we have already noted under the entry for bursa and cochlea, the inner ear contains a wealth of interesting names, such as the labyrinth, the scala, the utricle and the saccule, the incus, the malleus, the stapes, and the tympanic membrane.

The ear is divided into three compartments: the outer ear, the middle ear and the inner ear. The outer ear consists of the flap of skin stuck to the outside of the head known as the *pinna* (which means "a feather or fin"), the auditory canal and the eardrum. Beyond the eardrum there is a cavity called the middle ear, containing a chain of three tiny bones or ossicles, the smallest bones in the human body. They are the *malleus*, the *incus* and the *stapes*.

Malleus means "hammer or mallet" in Latin, *incus* means "anvil" and *stapes* means "stirrup". They look remarkably similar to the objects they are named after, especially the stirrup.

Sound waves make the eardrum vibrate. These vibrations are transmitted to the *manubrium* (the "handle") of the hammer, which in turn relays them to the anvil, which then sends them on to the stapes. Each step amplifies the vibrations of the eardrum along the way. The stapes transmits the amplified vibrations of the eardrum to the cochlea, a shell-like structure in the inner ear that houses the organ that is responsible for turning pressure waves into electrical signals that can be processed by the brain.

Related words

As mentioned in the chapter on the malleoli, the word *malleus* gave us **mallet**, **malleable** and **maul**.

The word *stapes* is distantly related to "step", a stirrup being a step that allows one to mount a horse. The peroneal tendons are known as the stirrup tendons because they travel under the foot like the footplate of a stirrup.

The word *incus* comes from *cudere*, meaning to strike, and is distantly related to the verb "to hew", meaning to chop with an axe. The word *incus* is also used in meteorology, the science of the weather, to describe anvil-shaped thunderstorm clouds, technically known as a *cumulonimbus incus*.

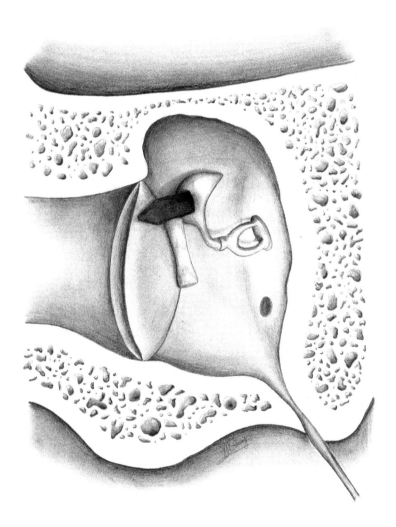

THE MASTOID PROCESSES

Even men have at least four breasts... well, breast-like structures. We all have two mastoid processes, which you can feel at the base of the skull, just behind your ears. Mastoid comes from the Greek *mastoeides* meaning "shaped like a woman's breast". The illustration shows the skull seen from below, giving a nice view of both breasts.

The Latin word for "breast or nipple", *mamma*, is also found in certain anatomical terms. The mammary gland is an obvious one. Interestingly, the mammary glands are actually modified sweat glands that are functional only in females. Well, this is certainly the case for humans, but male lactation is common in some species of animals such as certain fruit bats and some flying foxes.

The mammillary bodies on the other hand are small nipple-like structures located on the underside of the brain, that can be seen in the illustration of the *pons* a few pages away. The mammillary bodies are involved in memory, and can be shrivelled in people with chronic alcoholism, leading to impaired memory.

Related words

A **mastodon** is a prehistoric elephant with nipple-like lumps on its teeth used for grinding up vegetation.

A **mastectomy** is the removal of a breast or part of a breast, usually to treat breast cancer. Some believe that the Amazons, an ancient Greek tribe of warrior women, performed a unilateral mastectomy to avoid any hindrance when drawing a bow.

Gynecomastia is the technical term for enlarged breasts in males, or man-boobs. Gynecomastia literally translates as "woman breasts". Man breasts would be "andromastia".

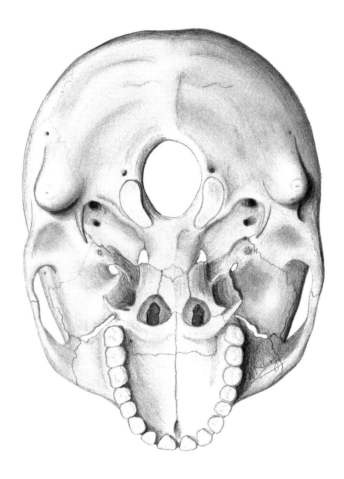

THE MENISCI

We have already discussed the lunate bone, a small, half-moon shaped wrist bone. The meniscus is the second moon-related body part. While the word "lunate" is based on the Latin word for moon, *luna*, the word "meniscus" is based on the Greek equivalent, *mene*. The diminutive *meniskos*, which means a crescent moon, was adopted by modern scientists to refer to several crescent-shaped things. There are for instance the crescent-shaped pieces of cartilage in the knee that act as stabilisers, lubricators and shock-absorbers when walking, running and jumping. The illustration shows the top of the tibia seen from above, with the two crescent-shaped menisci sitting on top. The menisci can get torn and, as usual, surgeons have come up with graphic ways of describing the different kinds of tears. According to the shape of the injury, you can end up with a bucket handle tear or a parrot beak tear for example. Another word for the menisci is the "semi-lunar" cartilages.

The word "meniscus" is also used in optics to describe the shape of lenses that are concave on one side and convex on the other, like a crescent moon. If you are wearing glasses, you are probably looking through meniscus lenses.

If you have any memories of your chemistry classes at school, you might remember that when you put water in a test tube it curves upwards at the edges, forming a meniscus. This phenomenon is caused by the fact that water molecules stick to glass better than they stick to each other, so they tend to climb up the edges of the glass test tube. Water forms a concave meniscus, where the water level is lowest in the centre of the test tube whereas other liquids, like mercury, form a concave meniscus that bulges in the middle.

Related words

The Greek word for **moon**, *mene,* is related to the Latin word *mensis*, meaning **month**, for obvious reasons. Thus, there are many words in use today that indirectly come from the Greek word for moon, like **menstruation** and **amenorrhea** for instance. On the subject of menstruation, Natalie F. Joffe published an entertaining article in 1948 entitled "The Vernacular of Menstruation" that lists the different ways of saying that women are on their period: my read-headed aunt from Reading, the hammock is swinging, Mickey Mouse is kaput, and all is not quiet on the waterfront to name but a few.

Monday is the day of the moon.

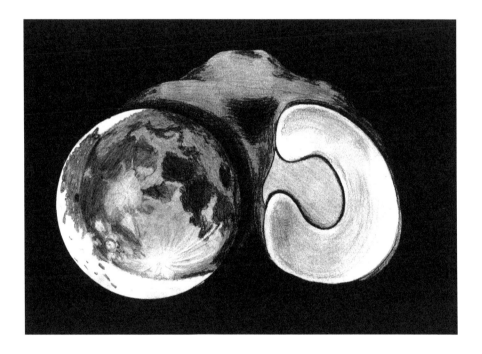

THE MITRAL VALVE

It is amazing to think that it is only since the 17th century and the works of William Harvey that we have known that the heart is the organ that pumps blood around the body. Before then, the heart was given many functions: a blood-producing organ, a heat source for the body, the seat of intelligence and the seat of the emotions.

The heart actually consists of two small pumps (the *atria*, meaning the entry halls) and two larger pumps (the *ventricles*, meaning the little bellies). Between the atria and the ventricles there are valves that let the blood circulate in one direction but prevent it from going back in the opposite direction. The cusps of the valves are attached to the heart by *chordae tendineae*, literally tendinous ropes, and colloquially known as heartstrings. The heartstrings are attached to *papillary* muscles, which literally means "nipple-like" muscles.

The valve between the right atrium and right ventricle is called the tricuspid valve because it has three points of attachment in the ventricle. The valve between the left atrium and left ventricle only has two points of attachment in the ventricle, and has been given the name *mitral valve*. The mitral valve is so called because it looks like a mitre, the two-peaked headgear worn by bishops and popes. Funnily enough, the word "mitre" comes from the Greek *mitra*, meaning "a turban".

The valves of the heart can be the seat of several heart conditions, such as mitral insufficiency for instance. Mitral insufficiency is not when the Pope has forgotten his hat, but when the mitral valve does not close properly. If the condition becomes serious enough, the valves can be replaced by artificial valves that are either made of metal or from a valve taken from a pig's heart.

Related words

In carpentry and woodworking, a **mitre joint** is a joint made from two pieces of wood cut at an angle, like the two peaks of the pope's hat. Usually, a mitre joint involves two pieces of wood cut at a 45 degree angle that fit together to make a 90 degree angle. Most picture frames are made with mitre joints for example. A **mitre saw** is a circular saw that allows you to cut at specific angles, and a **mitre block** is a tool that provides a guide for cutting mitres with a handsaw.

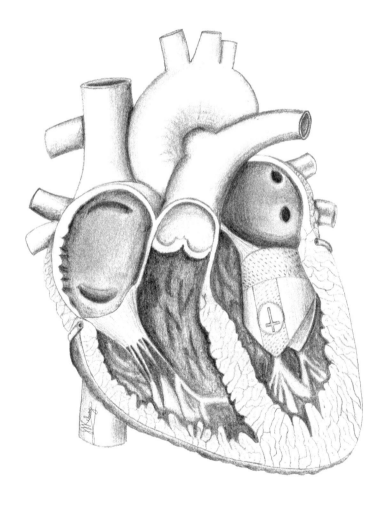

MUSCLES

Lots of muscles have interesting names, like the sartorius, the gracilis, the pectineus, the piriformis and the soleus to name but a few. The word "muscle" itself has a fascinating origin too: it comes from *musculus*, the diminutive of *mus*, Latin for "mouse". Thus, muscle actually means "little mouse".

Some people think that the name derives from the fact that contracting muscles look like rodents scuttling around beneath the skin. Another explanation is that some muscles, the long head of the biceps for instance, resemble a mouse with a long white tendon for a tail.

There are about six hundred muscles in the human body, the largest being the *gluteus maximus*, which admittedly sounds like the name of a Roman gladiator, and the smallest being the *stapedius*, a muscle that attaches to the *stapes*, one of the ossicles of the middle ear, the smallest bones in the human body. Muscles make up roughly forty percent of your bodyweight, but obviously this depends on whether you are muscular, slim or obese.

The muscles on the right hand side of your body are controlled by the left hand side of your brain and vice versa. That is why people who have had a stroke (that is to say a blocked or burst blood vessel in the brain) on the right hand side of their brain are sometimes paralysed on the left hand side of their body.

The muscle that you definitely do not want to stop working is your heart. It pumps over seven thousand litres of blood every day, and works non-stop, twenty-four hours a day for eighty years on average.

Related words

Most of the words that contain the root *myo* share the same origin. A **myocyte** is muscle cell, a **myopathy** is a muscle disease, **amyotrophy** is muscle wasting, a **myorelaxant** is a substance that relaxes muscle tissue, etc. An exception is "myopia", which is the technical term for short-sightedness, and does not share the same origin.

Mussels, the delicious bivalve molluscs, also get their name from the Latin word for mouse. However, the connection between the two animals is far from clear. Some people have conjectured that they got their name because their shells look like mouse ears, whereas others believe that the shells resemble the entire body of a mouse, both in size and colour.

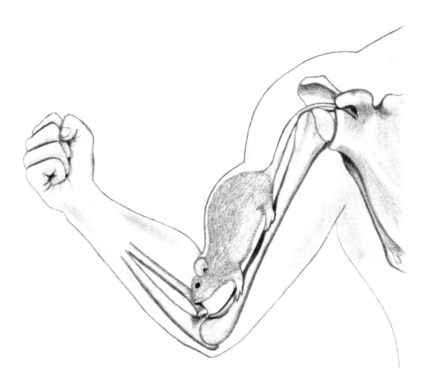

THE NAVICULAR BONE

There are four boat-shaped bones in the human body: one in each hand and one in each foot. This chapter is about the boats of the feet. The ones in the hands are named after the Greek word for boat, *scaphos*, whereas in the feet they are named after the Latin word for ship, *navis*.

The navicular bone is a bone that lies between the ankle and the big toe. It forms the keystone of the inner arch of the foot. A muscle in the calf called the tibialis posterior attaches to the navicular bone, and holds it up in its position at the top of the arch. In a condition called posterior tibial tendon dysfunction, the tibialis posterior tendon gets inflamed or torn, and is no longer able to hold up the arch of the foot, causing a form of flatfoot (adult acquired flatfoot).

Some people are born with an accessory navicular bone, a *sesamoid bone* located within the tibialis posterior tendon. It usually goes unnoticed but can become painful for some people.

Horses also have a sesamoid bone called the navicular bone, which is well known by veterinary surgeons because it is thought to be a major cause of lameness in horses.

Related words

A **navigator** is one who sails a ship, and the *navy* is the branch of the military that deals with warfare fought on water, in ships.

A **navvy** is an old-fashioned word for someone who constructs roads, railways and canals. It is short for "navigational engineer", and refers to the workers who would excavate canals by hand. Once the railway mania got under way, navvies started working on railways instead. In Europe, most work was done by hand, whereas in the United States they relied more on steam powered machines that also became known as navvies.

Another word for the belly button is the navel. It is completely unrelated to boats.

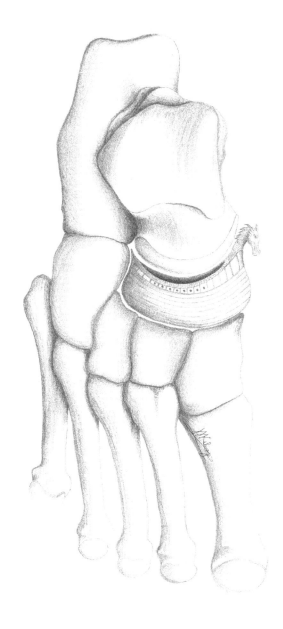

The Obturator Membrane

'There's a hole in my pelvis dear Liza, dear Liza.'
'So cover it with an obturator membrane dear Henry, dear Henry.'

The obturator membrane is a cover for the obturator foramen, a large opening at the bottom of the pelvis between the ischium and the pubis. It is almost totally blocked off by the obturator membrane. The obturator canal is an opening in the obturator membrane that allows the obturator nerve, artery and vein to leave the pelvis and enter the thigh. A muscle attaches to either side of the obturator membrane: the obturator internus on the inside and the obturator externus on the outside. In the illustration, the plug can be seen as the obturator membrane that blocks off the obturator foramen. The plug chain follows the path of the obturator internus muscle, curling round the ischium (the sit bone) before attaching to the top of the femur (the thighbone).

"Obturator" comes from the Latin verb *obturare* which means "to stop up or block up", like a plug in a sink hole. Surprisingly, the English verb "to obstruct" comes from a different Latin verb, *obstruere*.

Related words

Nowadays, the verb "to obturate" is still used as a technical term in some fields. If you are unlucky, you might have to undergo root canal obturation by your dentist. Engineers and plumbers can use obturator valves.
Some people have something called an oronasal fistula, that is to say a hole in the roof of the mouth that connects the mouth to the nasal cavity. These people can use a prosthetic device called a palatal obturator to block up the hole, allowing them to speak, eat and breath more easily.

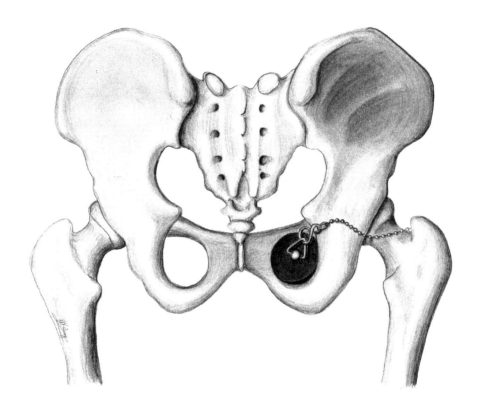

THE ODONTOID PROCESS

We have already discussed the origins of atlas, the first cervical vertebra. Atlas sits on top of axis, the second cervical vertebra, so called because it bears an odontoid process that serves as an axis of rotation for the atlas. The atlas can spin about 50° around this axis, The odontoid process literally means the tooth-like process, from the Greek *odon* meaning tooth. The odontoid process is sometimes called the *dens*, which means "tooth" in Latin.

Tooth enamel is famously the hardest substance in the human body. Unfortunately, the tooth of the second vertebra is not as resistant as its eponymous structures. The axis can be the seat of several types of fracture. For example, the whole tooth can break off, leading to what is known as a peg fracture. Fractures of the odontoid process cannot be viewed by X-ray in an ordinary position: they are viewed from the front through the open mouth of the patient.

Another fracture that the axis can sustain is called the hangman's fracture. A hangman's fracture is when both the lamina (literally the blades) or both the pedicles (literally the little feet) of the axis break. The term "hangman's fracture comes from the fact that people who are hanged often sustain this type of fracture. An experienced executioner would carefully place the noose and adjust the height of the fall so as to incur a high cervical injury that would cause immediate death, rather than let the prisoner die slowly from asphyxiation.

However, as noted by Dr. Ferris Hall from Harvard, "the more appropriate term is "hangee" fracture, because it is not the hangman who is injured. If medieval hangmen had suffered this fate every time they performed their duties, that entire profession would have been rapidly decimated, with presumed difficulty in recruiting a new workforce".

Related words

Dentistry and odontology are the fields that study teeth and their diseases.
A dandelion is a flower with jagged leaves that resemble a lion's teeth (from the French "dent de lion").
A trident is a three toothed pitchfork.

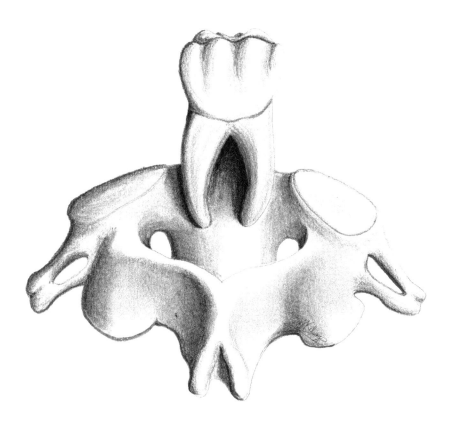

THE PARIETAL BONE

The cranium, that is to say the dome of the skull, is made up of six bones: a frontal bone in the area of the forehead, an occipital bone at the back, two temporal bones around the ears, and two parietal bones. The parietal bones form the side walls of the skull, and that is exactly where the word "parietal" comes from. *Paries* means "a wall" in Latin.

The names of the lobes of the brain are named after the overlying bones of the skull. The frontal lobe lies beneath the frontal bone, and is involved in things like planning ahead, calculating, problem solving and motor control. The occipital lobe is primarily involved in sight. The temporal lobes deal mainly in hearing, speech and memory. The parietal lobes process information related to touch and body position.

The most famously unlucky parietal bone is perhaps that of president John Fitzgerald Kennedy, that was shattered by a bullet on 22 November, 1963.

Some amphibians, reptiles and fish have a third eye, known as a parietal eye because it sits in a hole located between the two parietal bones of the skull. This parietal eye is thought to be evolution's earlier attempt at detecting daylight to regulate circadian and seasonal rhythms. In more recently evolved animals, the third eye seems to have disappeared to make way for more efficient photoreceptive machinery, like the intrinsically photosensitive retinal ganglion cells found in human eyes (for more information, see the chapter on the retina).

Related words

In the United States, **parietal rules** are rules and regulations that apply within the walls of a college dormitory (especially rules regulating visits from members of the opposite sex). In archaeology, **parietal art** is wall art as left by prehistoric humans on the walls of caves.

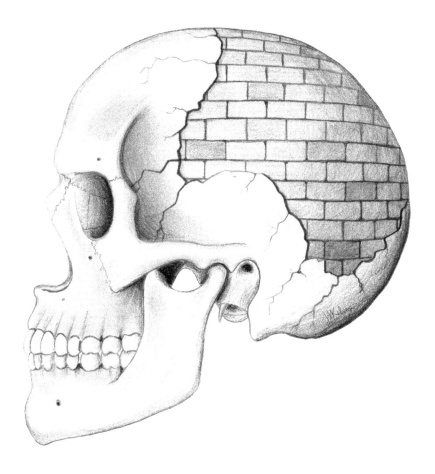

THE PATELLA

The *patella* is what medically-trained people call the kneecap. The word *patella* is the diminutive of the Latin *patina*, and means "little plate". The *patella* is a sesamoid bone that develops within the tendon of the quadriceps muscle.

The kneecap is not just a kind of cover that protects the knee joint, it is actually part of the knee joint and serves a much more useful purpose. It actually acts as a fulcrum that allows the quadriceps to straighten the knee more easily.

It is often stated as an amazing fact that babies do not have kneecaps. They do have kneecaps, but they are made of cartilage so they are not visible on an X-ray. Like a great many bones in the human body, kneecaps start off as cartilage and gradually ossify over the first couple of decades of life. As we have already noted in another chapter, the collarbone is the last bone to completely ossify between 20 and 25 years of age.

Some rare genetic disorders do leave people kneecapless, but they are still able to walk. They cannot however straighten their knees as fast or with as much force as kneecap-bearing individuals.

Ostriches are on the other end of the scale: they have two kneecaps in each knee. It is thought that this enables them to extend their knees even faster and with more force than most single-kneecapped animals. As a researcher from the Royal Veterinary College has pointed out, understanding why ostriches have two kneecaps could help us design better knee prostheses, or even help design better robots and exoskeletons.

Related words

A **paten** is a plate used to hold bread during the celebration of the Eucharist.

The word **pate** is slang for the top of the head. The word is of unknown origin but if you remove the top of the skull (à la Hannibal Lecter) you do end up with a plate or shallow bowl.

Thus, you have plates at either end of your body: a pate on top and two plates of meat at the bottom. (In cockney rhyming slang, feet are referred to as "plates of meat".)

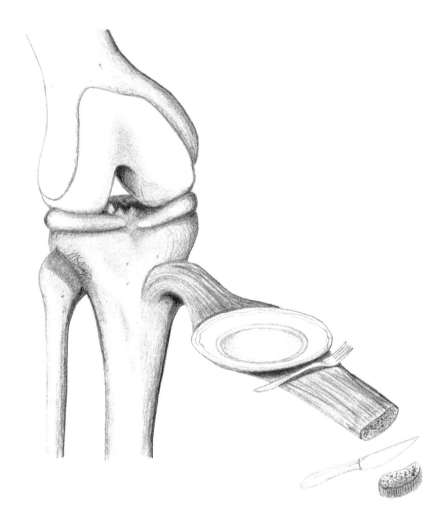

THE PECTINEUS

Have you ever wondered why pubic hair is so curly? Maybe it is because the pubic comb is inaccessible. The pectineus is a muscle located in the inner thigh, in the groin area. It is one of the five adductor muscles that allow you to squeeze your thighs together with enough force to crush a watermelon (as seen on the internet). The five adductor muscles are the adductor brevis (short), longus (long), magnus (great), gracilis (thin) and pectineus. Pectineus comes from *pecten*, the Latin word for "a comb".

The pectineus muscle inserts on the pectineal line of the pubis, sometimes called the pecten of the pubis. However, it is not clear why the pecten of the pubis was thought to be comb-like. Perhaps the pubis resembles a certain kind of old-fashioned comb, or perhaps combs were sometimes made from the pubis of animals, just as spades were made from scapulae and needles from birds' fibulae.

Related words

The adjective **pectinate** means comb-shaped. The antennae of certain moths can be qualified as pectinate for instance, as can the leaves of some plants, like ferns.

Scorpions have **pectines** on the underside of their bodies, comb-like organs that brush over the ground to detect substances, in the same way that other animals would use smell and taste.

Although the words "pectoral" and "expectorate" sound like they might be related, they have nothing to do with combs. Neither do the words "expect" and "expectation". They come from *pectus* meaning "chest" and *spectare* meaning "to look" (a root that can also be found in "spectacles" and "speculate").

Pectin is another word that sounds like it might be closely related, but is not. Pectin is the substance found in some fruits that makes jam set. The name pectin comes from the Greek word *pektos*, meaning "congealed".

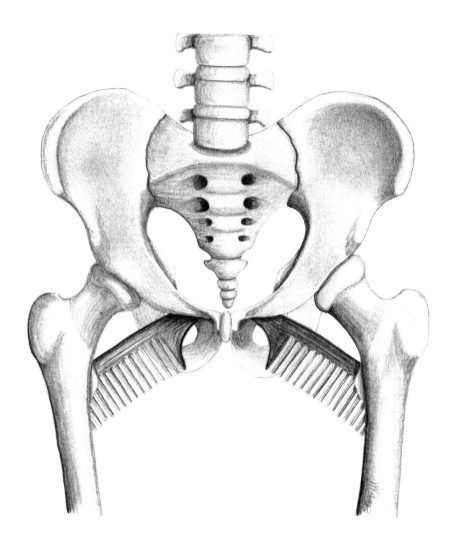

THE PELVIS

In the very first chapter, we discussed how the acetabulum, the socket of the hip joint, is actually a little vinegar cup that contains another, even smaller cup, the cotyloid fossa. This cup in a cup arrangement is part of the pelvis, a word that means a "bowl or basin" in Latin. So we have a cup inside a cup inside a bowl.

The pelvis actually made up of two halves, joined together at the back by the sacrum and at the front by the pubic symphysis. Each half is called an *os coxae* ("hip bone") and is in fact made of three bones. These three bones, the ilium, the ischium and the pubis, start off as three separate bones but gradually fuse together like the bones of the skull. By the age of 18, they are well and truly fused. The ilium is the large flat part of the os coxae that you can feel when you put your hands on your hips. The ilium should not be confused with the ileum (with an e), which is part of the small intestine. The ischium is the part we sit on, and the pubis can be felt just above the genitalia. The angle formed by the two pubic bones is acute in men but obtuse in women. It is one of the easiest ways to tell male and female skeletons apart.

In order for us to be able to walk on two legs, the human pelvis has gradually become narrower. This is excellent news for bipedalism, but not such good news for childbirth. As human pelvises got narrower, babies got harder to expulse. As a result, human childbirth is an exceedingly painful and risky affair compared with most other animals. The women who survived childbirth were those who gave birth earlier, to smaller, more supple, more immature babies. This is why human babies are born completely helpless compared to other animals, unable to look after themselves even for a few hours while their parents go shopping.

During pregnancy, the body releases a hormone called relaxin that, as its name suggests, relaxes the ligaments that hold the two halves of the pelvis together. This allows the pelvis to open up slightly to make way for the baby's head that is also flexible since the bones of the skull are not fused together yet. Even after childbirth, the two halves of the mother's pelvis do not return to their original pre-pregnancy position, making the hips look wider.

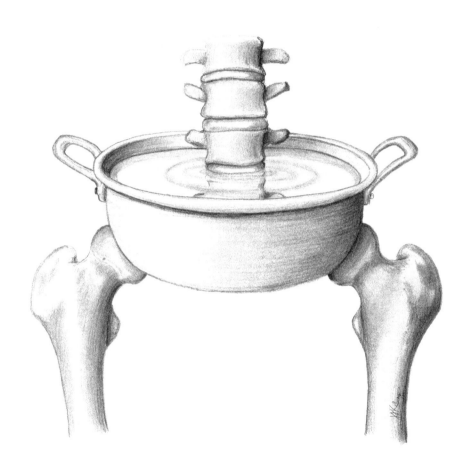

PENNATE MUSCLES

Muscles are made up of thousands of muscle fibres, also known as myocytes or muscle cells. Muscle fibres are bundled together into fascicles, a bit like the wires in a cable. "Muscle architecture" refers to the way in which the fascicles are arranged. If the fascicles are parallel, like those of the biceps for instance, the muscle is called "fusiform". If the fascicles are arranged in a fan shape like those of the chest muscle, the muscle is "convergent". Sphincters are muscles with circular fascicles that contract or relax to change the size of a circular opening (there is a sphincter that makes your pupil shrink in bright light for example).

Other muscles, known as pennate, pinnate or penniform muscles, have fascicles that are arranged like the barbs of a feather, as shown in the illustration. The word "pennate" comes from the Latin word *penna*, meaning "feather". This feather-like disposition means that the muscle fibres are shorter, but there are more of them, so a pennate muscle is able to produce more force than a similarly sized fusiform muscle.

Related words

The English word "pen" is related to *penna*. A *penna* was a feather, but also a quill, *i.e.* a pen made out of a sharpened feather.
Tube-shaped pasta with a pointy end is called penne because they resemble the sharpened tip of a quill. *Penne* is the plural of *penna*.
The visible part of the ear, called the auricle, is also known as the pinna, or feather.
Some leaves (palm leaves for instance) are referred to as pinnate or bipinnate because they have a similar structure to feathers.

THE PES ANSERINUS

And here comes another bird to add to our cabinet of curiosities. The *pes anserinus* is actually the name given to the conjoined tendon of three muscles that insert at the same place on the inside of the knee, close to the top of the tibia. The three tendons branch off from their insertion like the toes of a goose's foot, hence the name *pes anserinus*, which literally means "goose foot". The three conjoined tendons are those of the *sartorius*, the *semi-tendinosus* and the *gracilis* muscles. These muscles are sometimes referred to as the "guy ropes" of the leg because they help to stabilise the pelvis and knee.

The *semi-tendinosus* and the *gracilis* are often used by surgeons when performing ligament reconstruction surgery. They cut out, or "harvest", the tendons of one or both of these muscles and use them elsewhere in the body to replace snapped ligaments. They can be used to replace knee ligaments, ankle ligaments and shoulder ligaments amongst others. In most people, the tendons of the *semi-tendinosus* and *gracilis* slowly grow back after they have been harvested by the surgeon.

The *pes anserinus* can become painful in some cases. The pain can be due to pes anserine bursitis, a condition in which the *bursa*, the jelly-like sack that allows the tendons to slide back and forth across the shinbone, becomes inflamed and swollen. This condition is common in athletes, especially runners.

Related words

Pes has given us **pedestrian**, **pedometer**, **podiatrist**, **bipedal** and **pedal** to name but a few.

Anserinus has of course given us the scientific name of the goose family: the *anserinae*. It has also given the adjective **anserine**, which means pertaining to geese. It has also inspired the name of a protein, **anserine** (known as beta-alanyl-3-methyl-L-histidine to the layman), which was first discovered in goose muscle in 1929.

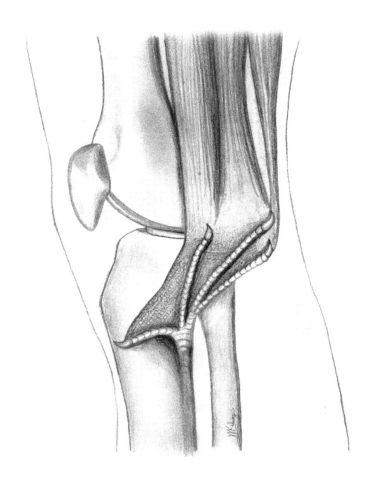

A PHALANX

When early anatomists came across the finger bones organised in little rows, they were reminded of soldiers in a line of battle. In ancient Greece, a phalanx was a military formation in which infantry would line up in close formation to make a wall of shields bristling with a hedge of spears. The Americans, of course, always have to have the best of everything, including the best phalanx. The United States military have developed the Phalanx CIWS (that stands for "close-in weapon system"), which is a radar-guided cannon that looks like R2-D2 from Star Wars.

We have a total of fourteen phalanges in each hand (three in each finger apart from the thumb that has only two), and another fourteen in each foot, making a total of fifty-six phalanges altogether, a veritable army. There are about 206 bones in the human body, more than a quarter of which are phalanges.

The length of the phalanges of your feet determines whether you have Egyptian, Roman or Greek feet. These are simply names we have chosen to describe different foot shapes, and in no way determine your origins, personality, susceptibility to disease or life expectancy, as some people would like you to believe.

The fingers and toes can be the seat of many injuries and deformities with expressive names: turf toe, trigger finger and trigger toe, mallet finger and mallet toe, jersey finger, hammer toe, claw toe, banana toe, mistle toe, etc. Alright, that last one is made up, but the rest are real.

Related words

Charles Fourier (1772-1837) was a French philosopher. He believed that something he called "**phalansteries**" would be the key to social success. His phalansteries were large buildings that would house communities of 1620 individuals who would cooperate (like the soldiers of a Greek phalanx) to create a utopian society. "Phalanstery" is a what is known as a portmanteau word formed by the association of "phalanx" and "monastery". Other examples of portmanteau words include *jeggings* (jeans and leggings), *brunch* (breakfast and lunch) and *Brexit* (Britain and exit).

THE PINEAL GLAND

Both the words "pineal" and "gland" have interesting origins, but we shall talk about glands in a different chapter. Pineal comes from the Latin *pinus*, meaning "pine", because the gland is similar in size and shape to a pine nut (and not a pinecone, as some people have hypothesised). Most structures in the brain come in pairs: you have two hippocampi and two amygdalae for instance, but only one pineal gland. It sits alone in the centre of the brain. Its position and solitary nature have led to several conjectures concerning its function throughout history. For example, Descartes famously thought that the pineal gland was the seat of consciousness and the place where thoughts were formed. This theory was later dismissed, because scholars reasoned that practically all mammals have a pineal gland, but of course they have no soul. The Egyptians allegedly associated the pineal gland with the eye of Horus and there is indeed a resemblance between the eye of Horus and the deep structures of the brain when seen in a sagittal section. Galen thought that it was as a valve that regulates the flow of a fluid he called "psychic pneuma" that filled the ventricles (cavities inside the brain that we now know to be filled with cerebro-spinal fluid).

Today, the pineal gland has been shown to be an endocrine gland that produces melatonin, a hormone that is involved in regulating circadian rhythms, *i.e.* the daily fluctuations in hormone levels and cellular activity (from *circa* meaning almost, and *dia* meaning day). When your circadian rhythm is out of synch with the day and night cycle, when you are experiencing jetlag for instance, taking melatonin can help to get your circadian rhythm back on track. It is sometimes considered to be a hormone involved in sleepiness, because melatonin levels rise at night. However, this is true in nocturnal animals as well. The truth is we do not really know why we secrete melatonin at night. Very few animals do not have a pineal gland, but still have circadian rhythms. There are even reports of people who, upon dissection, have been found to have no pineal gland, without suffering any ill effects throughout their lives. The third eye, mentioned in the chapter on the parietal bone, is closely linked to the pineal gland.

Melatonin should not be confused with melanin, the pigment that colours our eyes, hair and skin. Incidentally, the word "pigment" comes from the Latin verb *pingere* which means to paint. The *mela* in melatonin and melanin comes from the Latin word *melas*, meaning "black".

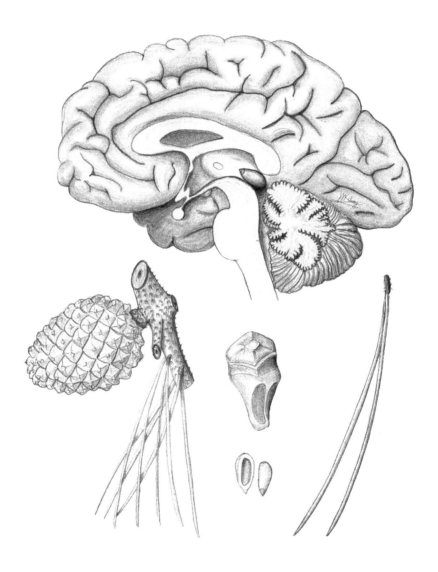

THE PIRIFORMIS

We have come across nuts and beans already, but this is the first fruit we have discussed in the human body ... although technically acorns and almonds are also fruits, but then so are tomatoes, aubergines and courgettes. Somebody really ought to think of another word to distinguish these fruits from the kind of fruit you would eat for desert. The piriformis is a deep gluteal muscle, which is a fancy way of saying an arse muscle. The word "piriformis" comes from the Latin word *pirum*, meaning "pear". It is literally the "pear-shaped" muscle. There are at least two other pear-shaped of piriform structures in the human body: the piriform fossa, which is an important landmark for surgeons operating on broken legs, and the piriform sinus, which is a recess in the larynx where food can get stuck. The piriform sinuses can also get injured by sharp objects such as fish bones. These injuries tend to give a feeling of having something stuck in the throat.

The piriformis muscle often (but sometimes wrongfully) gets the blame for buttock and leg pain. Indeed, the sciatic nerve travels very close to, or in some cases straight through, the piriformis muscle. The theory is that the piriformis muscle can compress the sciatic nerve and cause pain in all of the territories that the sciatic nerve innervates (the buttock and back of the thigh and leg).

The piriformis forms part of the rotator cuff of the hip, along with five other interestingly named muscles: the two gemelli ("the twins"), the two obturators ("the stoppers") and the quadratus femoris ("the square"). These relatively small, deep muscles stabilise the joint while the larger buttock muscles produce movement.

Something else that can be pear-shaped, but is rarely referred to as piriform, is people. Indeed, overweight or obese people are often categorised as either apple-shaped or pear-shaped, according to whether their fat has accumulated around their waste or around their buttocks and thighs. Strangely enough, being apple-shaped seems to be a lot worse in terms of the risk of developing cardiovascular diseases. This is because apple-shaped people have more of what is known as "visceral" fat, *i.e.* fat around their organs, which is more metabolically active than the subcutaneous fat of pear-shaped people. Subcutaneous fat lies under the skin but does not surround the organs so much, and is less metabolically active, meaning that it releases fewer hormones and molecules that create problems when they interact with other systems around the body.

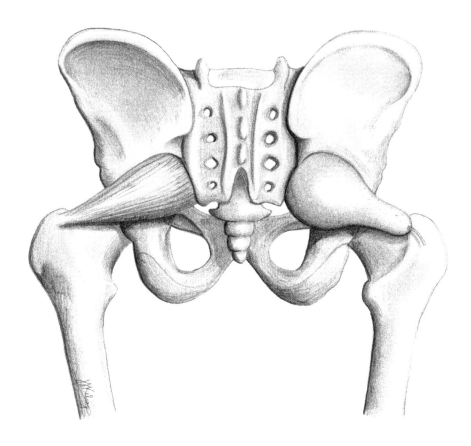

THE PISIFORM

As we have noted several times already, there are eight little bones in each wrist, most of which have interesting names. If you feel around in your wrist, at the base of the palm on the same side as the little finger, you might feel a small ball of bone that you can easily move about if you relax your wrist and fingers. This is the pisiform bone, or "pea-shaped bone", from the Latin word for pea, *pisum*. It is about the size and shape of a pea, but lacks the colour, unless there is something terribly wrong.

The word "pea" actually started off in English as "pease", as in pease pudding. People wrongly assumed that "pease" was the plural, and so made up the word "pea", a singular form of a word that was already singular. Similarly, people often mistakenly call the biceps the "bicep", and the quadriceps the "quadricep". This process of modifying a word that looks like a derivative to create another word is known as "back-formation". Other examples of back-formation include the verb "to edit", which came from "editor" and, ironically, the verb "to back-form".

Another similar class of words that are made from modifying existing words are "lost positives". Lost positives are words that have had their negative prefixes removed, often for comic effect. Gruntled, shevelled, couth, and combobulated are examples of lost positives.

The pisiform is in fact a *sesamoid bone* that is incorporated in the tendon of the *flexor carpi ulnaris* muscle, one of many muscles in the forearm that allow you to bend the wrist forwards, bringing the palm of the hand closer to the forearm. Incidentally, the word "palm" is also of interest. Some claim that the palm of the hand got its name from the practice of placing a palm leaf into the hands of victorious athletes in ancient Greece. However it seems more likely that palm trees got their name because their leaves are made up of thin leaflets that look like the fingers of a hand. The lines on the palm of the hand can be used for divination in an art known as palmistry or chiromancy.

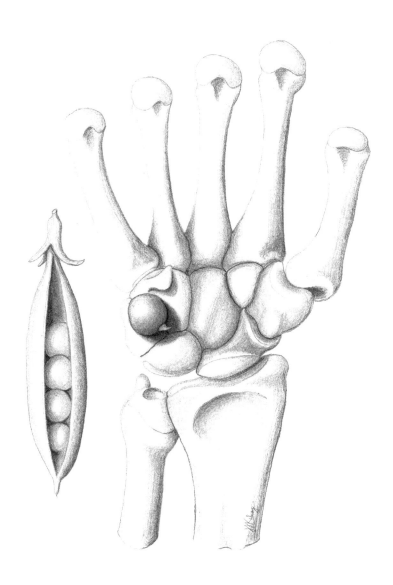

A PLEXUS

A plexus is any intertwined network of nerves or blood vessels. The illustration shows the brachial plexus in the neck and shoulder. Nerve roots emerge from the spinal cord and progressively branch off in several directions, mixing and mingling as they go along. A *plexus* in Latin is literally a "plait", from the verb *plectere*, meaning "to plait, braid, twine or fold".

There are four main nerve plexuses in the human body. The cervical plexus in the neck innervates some neck muscles. The brachial plexus innervates the muscles of the upper limb. The lumbar plexus and the sacral plexus in the lower back innervate the lower limbs and pubic region.

We also have a choroid plexus in the brain that produces cerebrospinal fluid, a transparent, watery substance in which the central nervous system bathes.

The solar plexus (or coeliac plexus) is an interlaced network of nerves, blood vessels and lymphatic vessels that lies just in front of the spine below the sternum. It has been given the epithet "solar" because the vessels of this plexus radiate outwards like the rays of the sun. The solar plexus itself comprises several smaller plexuses, like the splenic plexus, the gastric plexus and the pancreatic plexus. The solar plexus is particularly well known in boxing and self-defence, because blows to this area are notoriously painful. The solar plexus is also well known to those who practice Indian religions because it is the seat of the third primary chakra, known as Manipura.

So far we have limited ourselves to Greek and Latin origins. Now is perhaps the time to introduce Proto-Indo-European, a hypothetical language that was spoken sometime in the Neolithic era, and is the ancestor of all languages in Europe and India, with one notable exception being the Basque language, which appears to have developed in isolation. We get "plexus" from the Latin word *plectere*, which in turn comes from the Proto-Indo-European verb *plek*, meaning "to plait". However when one goes back this far in etymological history, one realises just how rich and complex our modern languages are compared to those spoken in the Neolithic. The root *plek* for instance is thought to have given us all of the following: accomplice, application, complex, complexion, complicate, complicity, deploy, display, duplex, duplicate, employ, explicate, explicit, exploit, flax, implicate, implicit, imply, multiply, perplex, plait, pleat, plexus, pliable, plight, replicate, reply, etc., etc., etc.

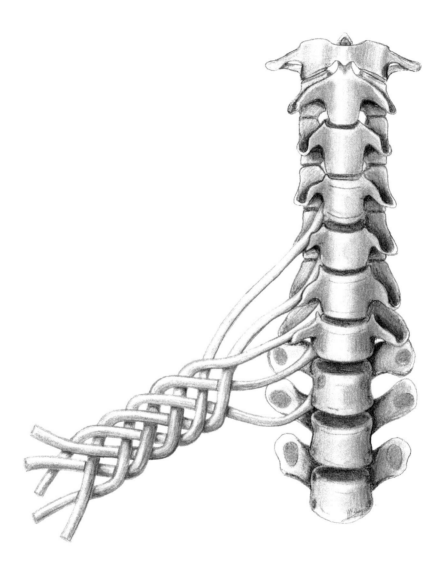

THE PONS

The central nervous system is composed of the brain, the cerebellum, the brain stem and the spinal cord. The brain stem comprises three parts: the medulla oblongata, the pons and the midbrain.

The 16th century anatomist who named the pons, Constanzo Varolio, thought that the pons was a structure that linked the two hemispheres of the cerebellum together, and that the medulla oblongata travelled beneath the pons like water under a bridge. The word *pons* is Latin for "bridge".

The pons is an information highway that connects the brain and the spinal cord to the cerebellum. It is also the starting point of many cranial nerves, and is a bit like the fuse box for the wiring that supplies the face.

Related words

A **pontiff** is a bridge-builder, from *pons* and *facere*, "to make".
There is a town in West Yorkshire, England, called **Pontefract**, meaning "broken bridge". There are many people, towns and places in the United States called **Pomfret**, a corruption of "Pontefract".
In some people, the atlas vertebra, *i.e.* the first cervical vertebra below the head, has an arch of bone that connects the lateral mass and the posterior arch. This arch is known as a *ponticulus posticus*, or "little posterior bridge".

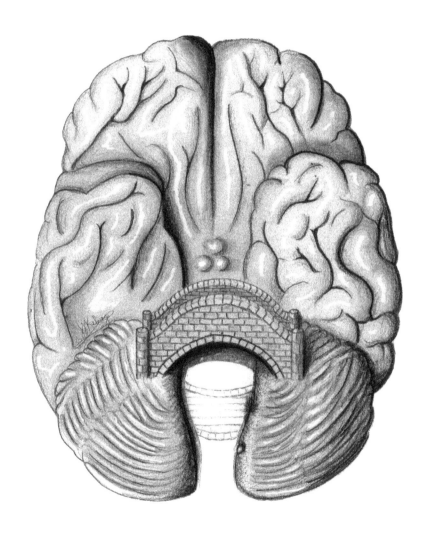

THE PTERYGOID PROCESSES

The sphenoid bone is located in the middle of the skull, and is perhaps the most complicated bone in the human body, on a par with the *temporal* bone. The name "sphenoid" itself has an interesting history, but here we shall focus on the two pterygoid processes of the sphenoid.

"Pterygoid" literally means "wing-shaped", from the Greek *pteryx* meaning "wing". In the illustration, the pterygoid processes are depicted as the downward beating wings of an owl. If you look at the shape of the sphenoid, you will see that the pterygoid processes are not really the most wing-like parts of the bone. The greater wings of the sphenoid however look very much like upward beating wings.

The medial and lateral pterygoid muscles attach to the pterygoid processes and help you to chew your food by moving your jaw up and down and side to side.

Related words

Pterosaurs are winged lizards.
Pterodactyls are pterosaurs with winged fingers.
Pteranodons are pterosaurs with wings and no teeth.
Lepidoptera are insects with scaly wings like moths and butterflies
Hymenoptera are insects with membranous wings like wasps, bees and flying ants.
Coleoptera are insects with sheathed wings, including all beetles.

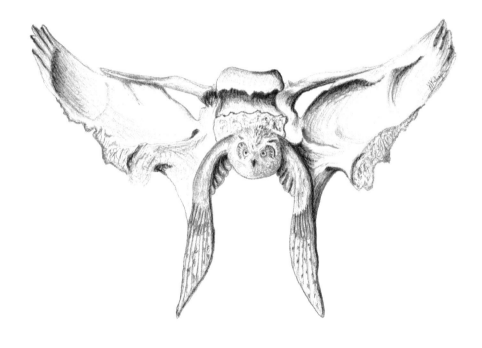

THE PUPIL

When you look into someone's eyes, you can see a tiny reflection of yourself in their pupils. The pupil was named in reference to this phenomenon: pupil comes from the Latin *pupilla*, the diminutive of *pupa* meaning girl or doll.

As mentioned in a previous chapter, the pupil is the opening in the centre of the doughnut shaped iris. The pupil can be constricted or dilated by the constrictor and sphincter muscles of the iris, respectively. When you are looking at something bright, your pupil constricts to regulate the amount of light that enters the eye. Pupil constriction is known as miosis. When you are in a dark room, your pupil dilates, which is known as mydriasis. When one pupil is more dilated than the other, this is called anisocoria. David Bowie is famous for having permanent anisocoria, because his left pupil was permanently dilated due to an injury to the muscles of the iris (allegedly incurred during a fight over a girl).

Although we humans tend to think of pupils as being round, they actually come in a vast variety of shapes throughout the animal kingdom. Cats, foxes and some reptiles like snakes and crocodiles have vertical slits for instance. Others, like hippopotami have horizontal slits. Others still have rectangular pupils, like goats and some cephalopods. Cuttlefish have extraordinary pupils that look like smooth, w-shaped squiggles. It appears that there are several hypotheses but no consensus as to why pupils come in so many different shapes. It is possible that vertical slits aid in depth perception for pouncing predators, whereas horizontal pupils are better for their prey that need a wide field of view. In fact, not even all humans have round pupils. Some people have malformations known as colobomas that result in a keyhole-shaped pupil.

Related words

A **puppet** is a doll that can be controlled by pulling on strings or, in a metaphoric sense, a person who can be manipulated.
Poppet is used as a term of endearment, but was once used to refer to the small human figures used in witchcraft.
A **pupa** is an immature insect. Larvae turn into pupae and pupae turn into mature insects. The pupa of a butterfly is called a chrysalis. The word "chrysalis" comes from the Greek word for gold, *chrysos*, because butterfly pupae often have a gold hue.
In French, a **"poupée"** is a doll. A **puppy** is a miniature toy-like version of a dog, just as a doll is a miniature human-like toy.

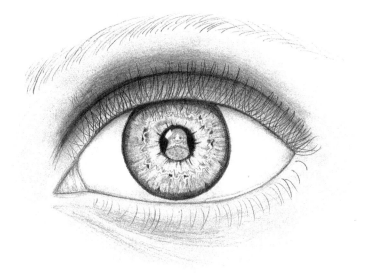

THE PYLORUS

We have already mentioned the antrum, the cave at the bottom of the stomach that food must enter before being allowed to continue on its way down the digestive tract. The pylorus is the sphincter that separates the antrum from the first part of the small intestine, the duodenum. *Pylorus* literally means "the gatekeeper".

Champagne is often said to go to your head quicker than other wines. This could be because the carbon dioxide dissolved in champagne relaxes the pylorus, allowing the alcohol contained in the stomach to flow into the intestines sooner. This enables the alcohol to be absorbed into the blood stream more quickly than the alcohol in a non-fizzy wine.

The pylorus is not only a barrier for food between the stomach and the intestine; it also seems to be the lower limit for sword swallowers as well. Amazingly, their blades successfully navigate through the mouth, oesophagus and stomach, but do not enter the duodenum. Interestingly, sword swallowers were instrumental in finding out how the stomach works. Early gastroenterologists asked sword swallowers to swallow metal tubes so that they could either look down the tube into the stomach, or send pieces of food down and retrieve them later on to study the effects of stomach acids.

Related words

The word **pylon** usually refers to a metal tower that carries high-tension electrical wires at a reasonably safe height. "Pylon" comes from *pyle* meaning "gate", perhaps because pylons resemble gateposts.

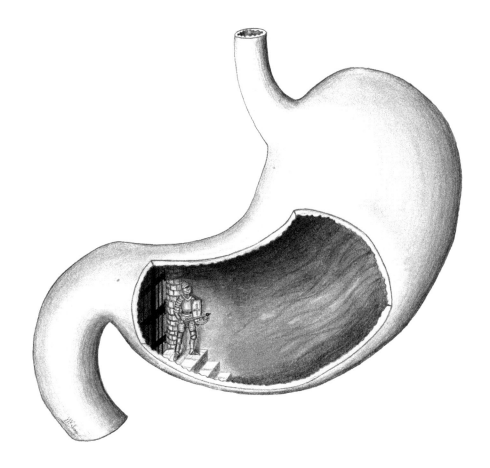

THE PYRAMIDALIS

Some people think that the abdominal muscles are six little rectangular muscles arranged like the squares of a bar of chocolate that would become visible if only they did enough sit-ups.

In fact the abdominal muscles are a group of five muscles, and the six bumps that you can see on people with a six pack are actually all part of the same muscle, the *rectus abdominis*. The other four muscles are the internal and external obliques, the transversus abdominis and the much less famous pyramidalis. The name of this muscle has rather an obvious origin. It is a small pyramid-shaped muscle that when contracted tightens the linea alba, the column of light rising from the pyramid in the illustration. The linea alba is a thin band of connective tissue that stretches from the xiphoid process of the sternum down to the pubic symphysis. It is the line that divides the left and right halves of your six pack (even if your six-pack is not visible). Everyone has a linea alba, but not everyone has a pyramidalis muscle. About one fifth of the population is pyramidalis-less, and others have only half a pyramidalis. *Linea alba* literally means the "white line", because it is made out of white connective tissue. Some anatomists have suggested that the pyramidalis might also assist penis erection.

There are other pyramids in the human body, this time in the brainstem, called the medullary pyramids. They are vaguely pyramid-shaped bulges in the medulla oblongata, the bottommost part of the brainstem. They are caused by bundles of nerves travelling down from the motor cortex to the spinal cord. The right motor cortex famously controls the left hand side of the body, and vice versa. Motor nerve fibres leave the right motor cortex of the brain and cross over to left hand side of the central nervous system at the base of the pyramids. The point where the fibres cross the midline is known as the pyramidal decussation.

Related words

The **pyramidalis** *arborvitae* is a kind of evergreen tree that is often found in gardens. Its name literally means the "pyramid-shaped tree of life".
A **pyramidion** is the capstone of a pyramid or obelisk.

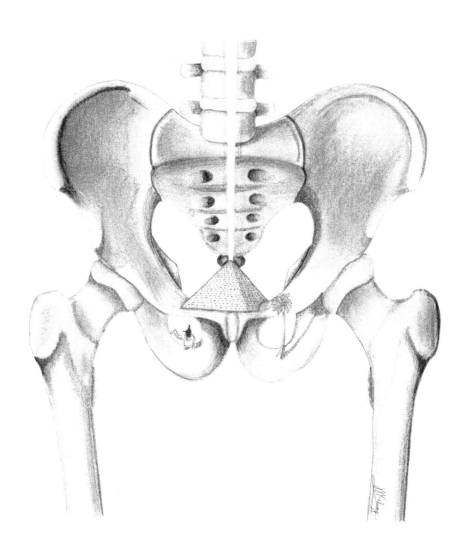

THE QUADRICEPS

Yes, there is a connection between the thigh muscle and Mount Rushmore. Can you guess what it is?

The answer is that both have four heads. The anatomically correct name for the thigh muscle is the quadriceps, which literally means "four heads". However, that is where the similarity ends. The four heads of the quadriceps are not called Washington, Jefferson, Roosevelt and Lincoln (although that is what I like to call mine). Instead, they are the vastus medialis, the vastus lateralis, the vastus intermedius and the rectus femoris.

Lots of muscles have more than one head: the biceps brachii, the biceps femoris, the triceps brachii, the triceps surae and the quadriceps for instance. Muscles with more than one head originate in several places but finish on a single tendon. Thus, even the singular form of "quadriceps" takes an -s. One thigh muscle is still a quadriceps, and not a quadricep, since the -s is there because there are four heads.

Well, this is what most people think. In fact, there are two extra, smaller muscles that can also be said to form part of the now inadequately named quadriceps: the articularis genu and the tensor vastus intermedius. The latter was only discovered in 2016, which just goes to show that we do not know all there is to know, even about the gross anatomy of the human body.

Related words

Most words that begin with quadri- or quadra- have four of something: **quadrant**, **quadruplets**, **quadrillion**, **quadrangle**, **quadriplegia**, etc.
The ending –ceps comes from the Latin *caput*, meaning "head". See the chapter on the capitate bone for more words related to caput.

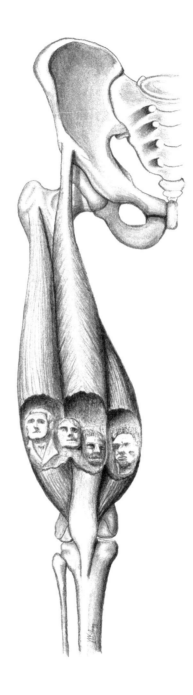

THE RADIUS

There are two bones in the forearm: the radius and the ulna. The radius goes from the elbow down towards the thumb, whereas the ulna goes down from the elbow towards the little finger. In Latin, a *radius* is the spoke of a wheel. Cart wheel spokes were often round on the end that inserts into the rim and rectangular on the end that inserts into the hub. The radius of the forearm is also round at the top and square-ish at the bottom. The radius (the bone) also bears a similarity to the radius of a circle: the radius bone is in fact the radius of the semi-circle described by the hand when you bend your elbow.

The bones of the forearm can sustain a number of fractures that have been given evocative names. A chauffeur fracture, or lorry driver fracture, is a fracture of the radial styloid process that got its name back when chauffeurs had to start their vehicles by hand using a crank. Chauffeur fractures often occurred when the car backfired, and are also known as backfire fractures.

A broken radius can result in a "dinner fork deformity", because the end of the forearm appears bent like the back of a fork.

A chisel fracture is a fracture of the radial head. On an x-ray, these fractures look as though they were caused by the blade of a chisel being knocked vertically down into the head of the radius.

Related words

Rays of sunlight *radiate* outwards from the sun like the spokes from the hub of a wheel. These rays of electromagnetic energy gave us the word "radio" as well.
Radiation radiates outwards from a radioactive substance, irradiating the objects and organisms that it touches.

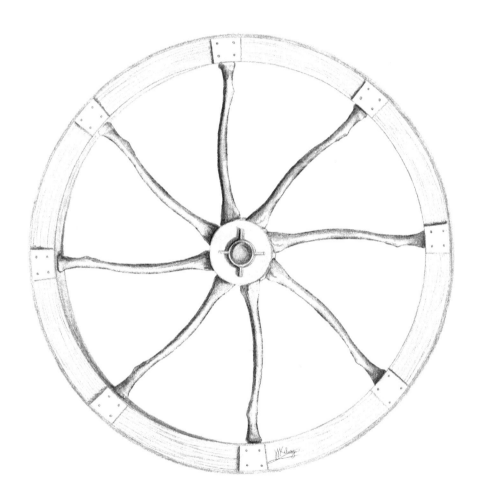

A RAMUS

The body is full of things that bear plant-inspired names. There are of course all the fruits and vegetables that we have already discussed: the piriformis, the fabella, the amygdala, the pineal gland and the glans penis. And there are still more to come, but there are also structures that have been named after the parts of a tree, like the cortex and the rami. A *ramus* is a Latin word for "branch".

Several structures have rami, but the champions of tree-related terminology are the nerves that emerge from the spine. Nerves leave the spinal cord in rootlets, which merge to form roots. Roots merge to make spinal nerve trunks, and trunks branch out into rami. Oddly enough, several rami then meet up and form more trunks which, after several more divisions, eventually turn into terminal branches. The illustration shows two spinal nerves and one spinal tree leaving the spinal cord.

Other vessels like blood vessels and lymphatic vessels have divisions called rami as well. Some people for instance have an extra artery in their hearts called the *ramus intermedius* coronary artery.

There are also bony branches in the jaw and the pelvis: the vertical parts of the mandible (the lower jawbone) are called rami, and so are both branches of the V-shaped pubic bone.

Our English word "ramification" comes from the same root.

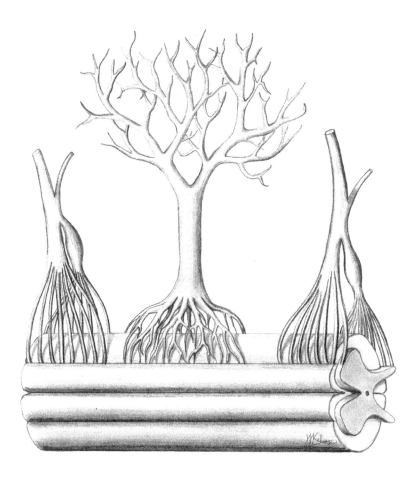

RANINE ARTERIES AND VEINS

Have a look in a mirror at the underside of your tongue. It is wet and slimy and bumpy, rather like the skin of a frog or a toad. The adjective ranine, (from the Latin *rana*, meaning "frog") means both pertaining to frogs (the amphibians not the French) and pertaining to the underside of the tongue. There are a ranine artery and a ranine vein under the tongue, also known as the deep lingual artery and vein. The diminutive *ranula* (Latin for "small frog") is the name given to a saliva-filled cyst that can develop on the underside of the tongue.

The tongue is a fascinating organ, and not just because of its amphibious connections. The tongue has several thousand taste buds that sit atop structures called papillae ("nipples" in Latin). These nipples can be mushroom-shaped (fungiform), leaf-shaped (foliate), thread-shaped (filiform) or surrounded by a wall (circumvallate). What is more, the distribution of these papillae and taste buds varies greatly from person to person, making tongue prints as unique as fingerprints and irises.

There are tongue maps that show which areas of the tongue detect different tastes. These maps are quite famous, but also quite famously wrong, because all areas of the tongue are in fact able to detect all five tastes: sweet, sour, salty, bitter and umami. All the other things we detect when eating are not in fact tastes, but flavours. Flavours are the result of the five tastes that we can detect with our tongues combined with the thousands of aromas that we are able to detect with our noses. That is why we can hardly taste anything when we block our noses. Flying in an aeroplane decreases our ability to detect flavours because the dry air evaporates our nasal mucus, temporarily deteriorating our aroma-detection system. Aeroplane chefs usually compensate for this by being very liberal with spices.

Related words

Ranidae is the scientific name for the frog family.
In some languages, like Italian and Spanish, "**rana**" means frog.

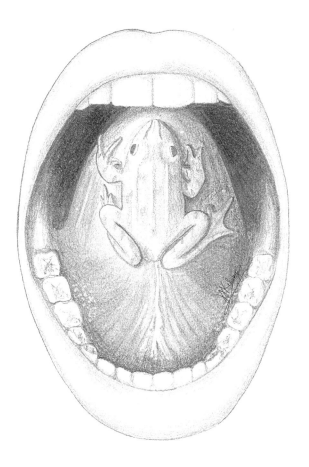

THE RETINA

Have you ever tried focusing the light from a television screen or a window on the opposite wall with a magnifying glass? This is exactly what happens in your eye. Light enters the eye via the pupil, which dilates and constricts to let in more or less light. Pupil dilation is known as myosis and pupil constriction is known as mydriasis. The light then passes through the *lens* (literally "the lentil", because of its biconvex shape), which changes shape in order to focus the image coming through the pupil onto the retina. The retina is the surface at the back of the eye that contains photoreceptors (light receptors) called rods and cones. The rods detect light intensity whereas the cones detect colour. There are three types of cones that each detect a different wavelength of light, corresponding to red, green and blue light. Together, these three primary colours combine to make all the other colours of the visible spectrum.

Recently, people called *tetrachromats* (meaning "four colours") have been shown to have a fourth type of cone which allows them to distinguish between hues of the same colour that would look identical to any person with the traditional three cones (*trichromats*). The retina also harbours a third cell type in addition to rods and cones. These cells have nothing to do with sight, yet they still detect light. They are very simply called "intrinsically photosensitive retinal ganglion cells", and are crucial for regulating our circadian rhythm by keeping the brain informed of the natural light and dark cycle. It is these cells that react strongly to the blue light of computer screens, and as a consequence trick your brain into thinking that it is still daylight at one o'clock in the morning when you are up watching videos on the internet.

Herophilus, an anatomist from Alexandria in modern-day Turkey, described the retina as being cobweb-like (or *arachnoeides*). It was later described as net-like, a *rete* being a kind of fishing net or casting net in Latin. The net-like appearance of the retina is due to the dense network of blood vessels that supply the back of the eye.

Related words

Something that is reticulate or reticular is literally net-like. There are various reticular fibres, networks, formations and systems in the human body.
Surprisingly, the word that we shall discuss in the next chapter, *retinaculum*, is unrelated to *retina*.

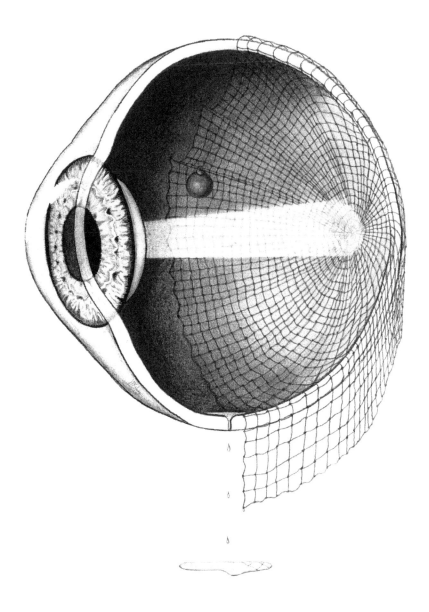

RETINACULA

Retinacula are bands of connective tissue that hold other structures, like tendons, in place. The word "retinaculum" comes from the Latin verb *retinere*, meaning "to retain". There are retinacula in the wrists that hold down the tendons of the flexor and extensor muscles. Many of these muscles originate at the elbow and go all the way to the ends of the fingers. Imagine what would happen if the tendons were not held down by strong retinacula. There are of course similar structures in the ankles that hold down the tendons of the muscles that move the feet.

There are retinacula in the knee as well, that hold the kneecap in place. Without these retinacula, the patella could easily leave the groove in the thighbone in which it slides up and down every time you bend and straighten your knee. The illustration is somewhat misleading because these retinacula do not actually cross over in front of the kneecap, but rather attach to the sides of the patella and to the top of the tibia. I would like to apologize to anatomists who might feel offended by this misrepresentation of such a fundamental structure.

Like practically every other structure in the human body, the retinacula can be injured and become the cause of pain. One common retinacular injury occurs when the kneecap is dislocated. When the patella leaves its groove, it can tear the medial patellar retinaculum that is supposed to hold it in place, resulting in joint instability. Of course, surgeons can repair it if they think it is necessary.

Related words

A **retainer** is a device used in dentistry to hold the teeth in place, usually after their position has been modified using a brace.

Water **retention** is when your body holds on to too much water. This causes swelling, often in the hands and feet. Water retention can be experienced on long-haul flights, where staying sat down for long periods of time allows fluid to pool in the feet and ankles. Flying also messes with your body in other ways, which you can found out about in the chapter on all things ranine.

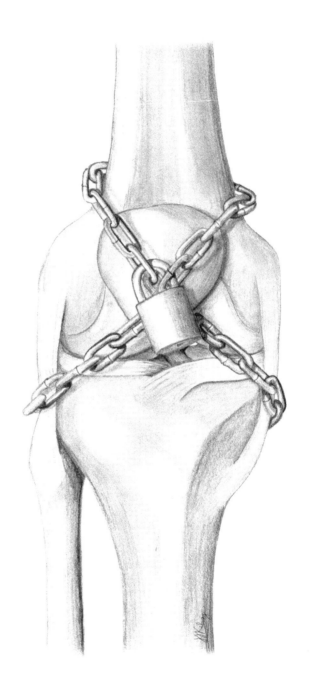

THE SACRUM

The sacrum is the largest bone of the spine and forms the back of the pelvis. This bone was first called the *hieron osteon* by the Greeks, and was literally translated to *os sacrum* (or "sacred bone") by the Romans a few centuries later. However, why the Greeks thought this bone was sacred has been the source of lengthy debates between etymologists for centuries. It seems that the sacrum was considered special or holy in several different cultures.

One explanation is that the holiness of the sacrum is related to Egyptian mythology. Seth killed his brother Osiris, cut him up into fourteen pieces, and scattered the pieces throughout Egypt. A temple was erected at each site where a part of Osiris's body was found. His spine was found at Busiris, and a great sculpture of what could be a representation of his sacrum was erected. The symbol of this column, shown in the illustration, is called the Djed pillar. The largest bone of the spine was considered especially sacred as it sits close to the reproductive organs and was thought to protect them.

According to Judaism, the Luz ("almond or nut" in Hebrew) is a bone in the spine from which humans will be resurrected. This bone is said to look both like an almond and the head of a snake. With a bit of imagination, the sacrum fits this description.

Muslims share a similar belief. According to Islam, there is a bone in the body that remains intact after death and does not decay. When the Resurrection begins, Allah will cause rain to fall which will make this bones grow until each person's body is restored to the way it was before they died. Some people think that, due to its size, the sacrum may resist decomposition more than other vertebrae and serve as the source of resurrection in the afterlife. However, it is widely believed that it is actually the coccyx that is referred to in this passage.

All of these explanations are poopooed by some, who suggest that the "hieron" in *hieron osteon* was mistranslated by the Romans and could just mean "strong or vigorous", not sacred or holy.

The sacrum is not only holy in the religious sense of the word. The sacral foramina are the eight holes shown either side of the Djed pillar. Spinal nerves emerge from these foramina. One of these nerves is called the pudendal nerve. Pudendal comes from the Latin word meaning "to be ashamed", because it is the nerve that carries sensation from the private parts that most of us are ashamed to show off in public.

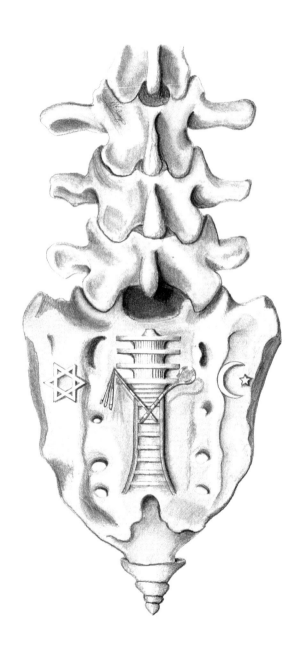

THE SARTORIUS

The sartorius is a long thin muscle of the thigh that originates on the anterior superior iliac spine of the pelvis and inserts on the tibia, forming part of the pes anserinus. It is the longest muscle of the human body. The name "sartorius" comes from the Latin word *sartor*, meaning "a tailor". In English, "sartorial" is an adjective used to refer to tailoring, clothes and style.

There are several explanations for how the sartorius got its name. The first and most convincing is that when both sartorius muscles contract, they bring the legs up into a roughly cross-legged position, similar to the working position that tailors once adopted. A second explanation is that the sartorius is very long and flat, and resembles a tailor's ribbon. A third explanation is that antique sewing machines required a strange kind of pedalling action that would solicit and develop the sartorius muscle in particular. Finally, a fourth and slightly less likely explanation is that the lower portion of the sartorius muscle roughly follows the inseam of a trouser leg... but only if your trousers end at knee length.

The sartorius is sometimes referred to as the "honeymoon muscle", because it flexes, abducts and laterally rotates the thigh, exposing the genitalia ready for honeymoon action. The gracilis muscle has the opposite action: it squeezes the thighs tightly together, and so is known as the "custodian of virginity", or a little less poetically as the "anti-rape muscle".

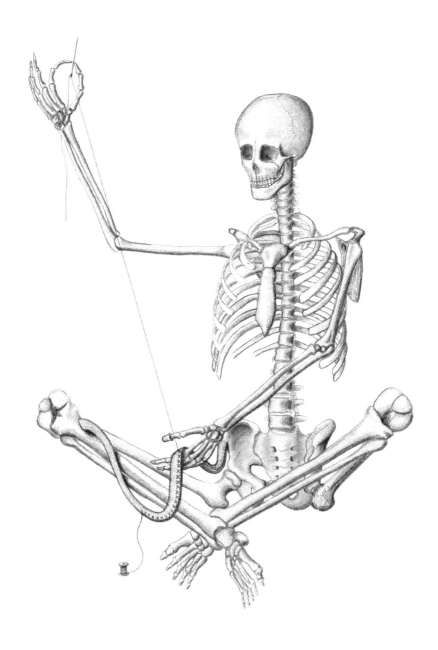

THE SCALAE

As we have already mentioned more than once, the inner ear is full of fascinating equipment. The exact way that hearing works is truly amazing, but is far too complex to go into in depth in one page. However, even the basic physiology of hearing is captivating. If you have read the chapter on the cochlea, you will remember that it is the snail shell-like case that contains the machinery that allows you to hear sounds. The cochlea is divided into three fluid-filled chambers, or scalae. A *scala* is a staircase in Latin. Indeed, each of the three chambers goes all the way from the base to the apex of the cochlea like a spiral staircase. In the illustration, the scala vestibuli would be below the staircase, the scala tympani would be above it, and the scala media would be the staircase itself.

Sound waves are transmitted by the eardrum to the ossicles of the middle ear: the malleus, the incus and the stapes. These tiny bones amplify the vibrations of the eardrum. The stapes pushes up against an opening at base of the cochlea called the oval window, which makes a wave in the fluid inside the cochlea. How far these sounds make it up the staircase depends on their pitch. Low-pitched sounds with low frequencies make it all the way to the top of the staircase, climbing two or three steps at a time as it were. High-pitched sounds with high frequencies on the other hand waste all their energy at the bottom of the staircase and barely make it up the first few steps. If the wave makes it to the top of the staircase, hair cells at the top of the cochlea will be stimulated and will generate an electrical signal that will be sent to the brain. The brain will interpret these sounds as deep, low-pitched sounds because the activity came from the apex of the cochlea. If the signal had come from the base of the staircase, the brain would interpret the sound as high-pitched.

Related words

Scaling a mountain would be easier with a staircase.
Scales can be used to rate almost anything. A scale of one to ten has ten steps or levels to choose from.
Ascend and descend also share the same etymology.

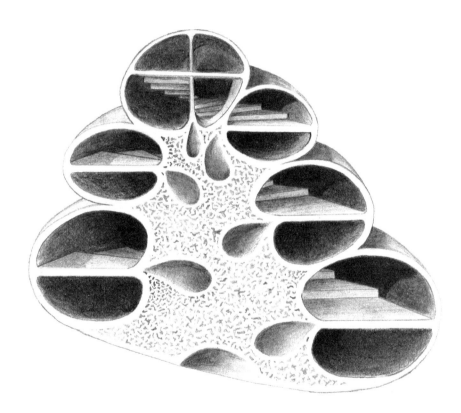

THE SCAPHOID

The scaphoid is our second boat-shaped bone, the other being the navicular bone of the foot. As usual when there are two similarly shaped structures in the body, one has been given the Latin name and the other has been given the Greek name. "Scaphoid" comes from the Greek *scaphos*, meaning "boat", whereas "navicular" comes from the Latin equivalent *navis*. This is also the case for the lunate bone and the meniscus (both are moon-shaped), the ethmoid bone and the cribriform plate (sieves), the acetabulum and the cotyloid fossa (cups), the pterygoid processes and the ala (wings).

The scaphoid bone is one of the eight carpal bones of the wrist. It forms the base of what is known as the anatomical snuffbox. When you make a thumbs-up sign, you will notice that this creates a depression between the tendons that lead up to the thumb on the side of your wrist. This is where snuff, or ground tobacco leaves, used to be placed before being inhaled.

A fall on an outstretched hand, or FOOSH as doctors tend to call it, can cause the scaphoid to break, resulting in pain in the anatomical snuffbox. Scaphoid fractures are notorious because complications during the healing process are very common.

Related words

As explained in the chapter on sutures, the sutures of the skull can fuse too early, before the brain and skull have stopped growing, in a condition called craniosynostosis. This resulting deformity depends on which suture has fused. **Scaphocephaly** occurs when the sagittal suture closes too early. Scaphocephaly literally means "boat head" because in this condition the head becomes elongated like the hull of an upturned boat.

Scaphism is a particularly gruesome form of torture that may or may not have actually been put into practice, but which is described in ancient texts. The victim would be tied up in a cage made of two small boats placed gunwale against gunwale, and left in the hot sun. Every day, they would be fed milk and honey, and their bodies would be covered in the same mixture. This would attract flies, insects, rats and other vermin that would slowly pick away at the victim's body until they died. Of course, they were not allowed a toilet break, so their cage became more and more insalubrious each day.

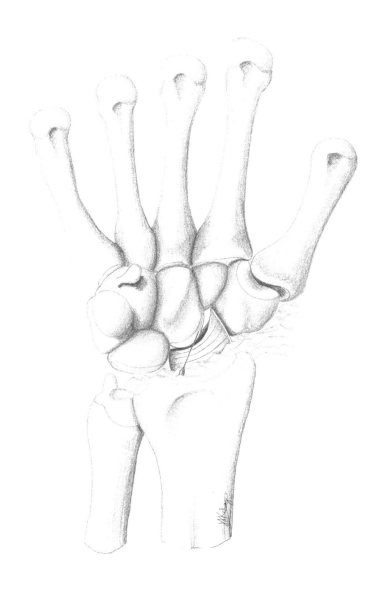

THE SCAPULA

Shoulder blades should perhaps more appropriately be known as "shoulder spades". Indeed, the official name for the shoulder blade is the scapula, a word that comes from the Greek word *skaptein* meaning "to dig". This is because if you tie an animal's shoulder blade to the end of a stick, it makes a decent spade, or at least Stone Age humans thought so. Some old anatomy texts refer to the scapula as the *pala*, which is a Latin word for "spade".

Shoulder "blades" is not a bad description either however. Native Americans used to make a variety of sharp-edged tools from the scapulae of bison, deer and elk. Archaeologists have found hoes, scrapers, sickles, squash knives and saws, all made from this same bone.

The scapula is a flat, roughly triangular bone that changes position by gliding across the ribcage in order to maximise shoulder strength and mobility. The scapula serves as an attachment point for eighteen muscles that can either move the scapula around or stabilise it while other muscles use it as an anchor point.

Sometimes, a scapula can become "winged", meaning that it sticks out like a wing rather than lying flat against the ribcage. This usually occurs when one of the muscles that hold the scapula down against the ribcage becomes paralysed. Paralysis of the interestingly named serratus anterior muscle is a common cause of scapular winging.

Related words

We have already come across arachnomancy and palmistry, and we will soon be discussing astragalomancy. There is also something called **scapulimancy**, which is the art of divination by observing scapulae. Scapulimancy was one of the seven forbidden arts in Renaissance magic (along with hydromancy, aeromancy, geomancy, chiromancy, pyromancy and necromancy).
Scapula is distantly related to **scoop**, **scab** and **scabies**.

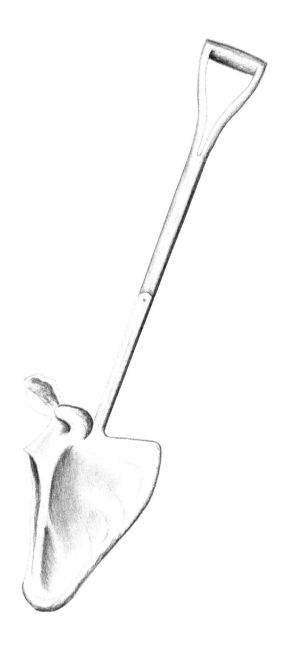

THE SELLA TURSICA

The sella tursica is another feature of the oddly-shaped sphenoid bone, and is probably one of the most bizarrely specific words that anatomists have come up with. The sella tursica is a little cavity in which the pituitary gland sits, as if in a saddle. But not just any saddle, a specifically Turkish saddle, for that is what the term *sella tursica* means in Latin. This is because like a Turkish saddle, the sella tursica has a particularly high pommel and cantle.

The jockey that sits in the Turkish saddle is the pituitary gland, a pea-sized gland at the base of the brain that for a very long time was thought to be just a little bag of slime, a pouch of nasal mucus that drained from the brain. Its very name comes from the Latin *pituita* meaning "phlegm or slime". More recently however, the pituitary gland went from being a ball of phlegm to being the master gland of the human body, secreting hormones involved in a plethora of different processes like growth, blood pressure regulation, kidney function and sexual function.

Tumours can sometimes cause the pituitary gland to secrete too much growth hormone. Gigantism is a condition caused by having too much growth hormone before the bones have finished growing. Robert Wadlow, who stood at 2.72 m tall (8 ft. 11 in), is probably the best-known case of gigantism. However, if you have too much growth hormone *after* your bones have finished growing, only your hands and face will continue to develop, resulting in a condition called acromegaly. A well-known case of acromegaly is the French wrestler and actor, André the Giant, who played the giant Fezzik in The Princess Bride and who, like many people with acromegaly, also manifested gigantism. He was 2.24 m (7 ft. 4 in) tall and weighed 236 kg (520 lb).

Yet another interesting feature of the sphenoid bone is the clinoid processes that surround the *sella tursica* like the bedposts of a four-poster bed. And "bed-shaped" is exactly what clinoid means, from the Greek word *kline* meaning "bed". So the pituitary gland can either be seen as riding the sphenoid bone in its Turkish saddle, or as reclining in a four-poster bed. "Clinoid" shares the same root as "clinical", which literally means "relating to the sickbed". Clinophilia is something many adolescents suffer from: a love of remaining in bed.

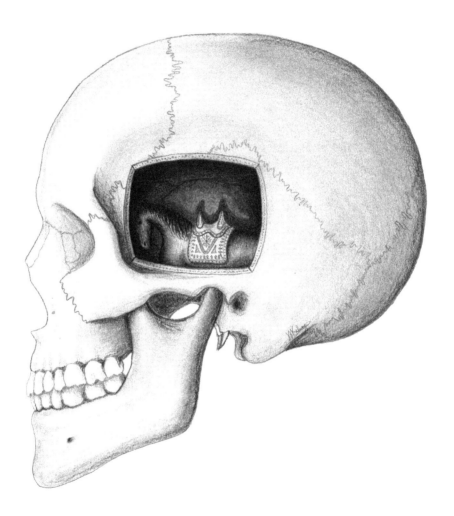

THE SERRATUS ANTERIOR

The body is a dangerous place to live: there are swords and sickles, soldiers and shields, blades and hammers, hooks and needles. There are also several saw blades. The serratus anterior, serratus posterior superior and serratus posterior inferior are all named after the Latin word for "saw", *serra*. These muscles are flat like a saw's blade, and attach to the ribcage by several pointy insertions that resemble the teeth of a saw.

The saw in the illustration is the serratus anterior, the muscle that pulls the shoulder blade forward (or "protracts" it) when you reach out in front of you. For this reason, the serratus anterior is sometimes called the "big swing muscle" or the "boxer's muscle" because it protracts and stabilises the scapula when you throw a punch.

In very lean or very muscular people (boxers are in fact a good example), the serratus anterior is clearly visible next to the chest muscles. The serratus anterior can be so developed that the individual teeth of the saw can be mistaken for ribs.

The serratus anterior can sometimes become paralysed, which results in scapular winging, a condition where the shoulder blade is no longer held down against the ribcage but sticks out like a wing.

Related words

Saw blades are of course **serrated**, meaning that they have tooth-like **serrations**.
The **Sierra Nevada** is a jagged mountain range that looks like the teeth of a saw blade.
Sierra Leone, the African country, is also named after its saw-tooth-like mountains.

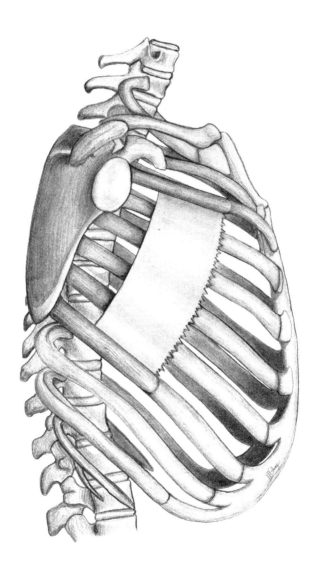

SESAMOID BONES

Sesamoid bones are bones that are embedded within a tendon. Most sesamoid bones are rather small, which is why they are called *sesamoid*, meaning "like a sesame seed". We have many sesamoid bones all over our bodies, particularly in the hands and feet, and some people have more than others.

The illustration shows the metatarsophalangeal sesamoids that lie beneath the base of the big toe, embedded in the tendon of the muscle that bends the big toe called the flexor hallucis brevis. We have two similar sesamoid bones at the base of the thumb.

The largest sesamoid bone in the body is the kneecap, which is embedded in the tendon of the quadriceps. The kneecap, like most sesamoid bones, actually serves as a kind of pulley to increase a muscle's ability to transmit forces by altering the direction of pull.

Some sesamoid bones, like the ones under the big toe, undergo enormous amounts of pressure. They can become painful in a condition called sesamoiditis, when the tendon surrounding the bone becomes inflamed. The pea-shaped pisiform in the hand is another sesamoid bone that can be injured: fractures can occur during a fall on an outstretched hand for instance.

The illustration also shows what a sesame seedpod looks like, for those, like me, who had no idea where sesame seeds come from. Incidentally, it is thought that the magical phrase "Open sesame!" from Arabian Nights, could come from the fact that sesame pods split open to reveal their treasure when they reach maturity.

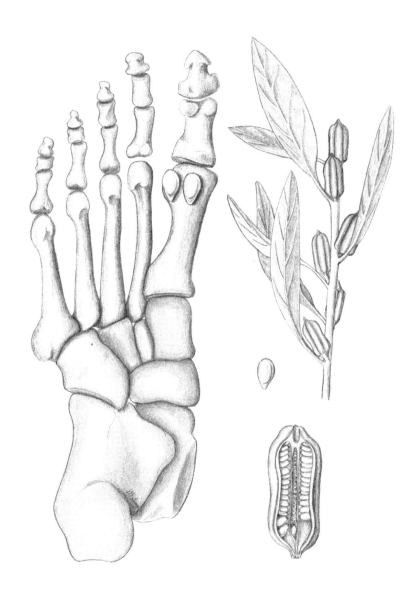

THE SOLEUS

The soleus is a muscle in the calf that lies beneath the gastrocnemii, the two large bulges at the back of the leg that we usually think of as the calf muscles. Although we have already come across many animals hiding away in the names of body parts, the soleus is the only structure in the body that gets its name from a fish (the carpal bones of the wrist have nothing to do with carp by the way). The word *soleus* means "sole", a kind of flatfish, in Latin. The soleus muscle was given this name because it is wide and flat like a flatfish.

The soleus is one of the calf muscles. It lies beneath the two easily recognisable heads of the gastrocnemius muscle, hiding away like a flatfish under the sand.

Soles are amazing fish, and not just because of their culinary potential. Like other flatfish, they start life as ordinary two-sided fish with eyes on either side of their head. After a few weeks, just as they start getting used to swimming around in a symmetrical body, one of their eyes suddenly decides to migrate over to the other side of their head, distorting their skull in the process. They gradually topple over and start swimming at an angle. One of their sides begins to darken to match the colour of the seabed while the other loses its colour and becomes white. Once they have become completely asymmetrical, they descend to the sea floor and settle into to their new life as bottom-feeders. In modern flatfish the eye has made its way all the way round to the other side of the body, but fossils of adult flatfish have been found that show the intermediate steps of this bizarre evolutionary adaptation. These fossils have eyes that have started to migrate but have only made it part of the way around the head.

Related words

The related Latin word *solum*, meaning "bottom or ground", also gave us the sole of the foot, the sole of a shoe, and soil.
The flatfish actually gets its name from a kind of flat Roman sandal that were also called *solea*.

THE SPHENOID BONE

As we have already mentioned in the chapter dealing with the pterygoid processes, the sphenoid is a strange shaped bone that sits in the centre of the skull. The sphenoid bone has an unusual name, because it looks absolutely nothing like the thing it is named after. In Greek, the word *sphenoid* means "wedge-shaped". The sphenoid bone is anything but wedge-shaped, however. A more plausible explanation is that it was initially called the *sphecoid* bone, with a –c, and *sphecoid* eventually became *sphenoid* due to translation or copying errors. *Sphecoid* means "wasp-like", from the Greek *sphex*, meaning "wasp".

This name seams much more appropriate, since the sphenoid does strongly resemble some kind of flying insect. Another clue to this origin is the fact that many parts of the sphenoid bone are named after the parts of an insect or flying animal. There are the pterygoid processes (literally "wing-like" processes in Greek), the greater and lesser ala (more wings, in Latin this time) and the rostrum (the snout-like or beak-like feature of some insects).

The sphenoid bone also has some other interestingly named features like the clinoid processes and the sella tursica. Go to the chapter on the sella tursica to find out more.

Related words

Sphex is the scientific name of a species of wasp, the digger wasp.
Sphenodons are wedge-toothed lizards, also known as tuataras. The tuatara is also remarkable for its third eye, or parietal eye, that is discussed in more detail in the chapter on the parietal bone.

THE SPINE

The spine is a thorny rose growing in a forest of spinal nerve trees. As noted in the chapter on rami, the divisions of the spinal nerves all bear tree-related names (rootlets, roots, trunks and branches). These spinal nerves emerge from the spine, a word which comes from the Latin *spina*, meaning a "thorn". The connection presumably comes from the fact that the spine is a stack of 33 vertebrae, each of which has pointy projections called spinous processes, which makes the spine resemble a thorny bramble or the spiky stem of a rose. Many of the structures that surround the spine get their name from these spinous processes: the spinal cord, spinal nerves, spinal discs, the erector spinae muscles, etc.

The 33 vertebrae of the spine are separated by discs of cartilage that tightly join the vertebrae together while allowing for movement. People tend to think of the spine as an unstable stack of bones and discs that can easily slip out of place like the blocks in a game of Tumbling Towers. This could not be further from the truth, but nevertheless some health professionals spread this kind of false information to attract more customers. The spine is extremely mobile and yet incredibly resistant, and you would be hard pressed to truly displace a vertebra, let alone manipulate it back into place with a satisfying pop.

Related words

A **porcupine** is a thorny pig (from the French "porc épic").
Spinosaurus is a thorny dinosaur, and its name literally translates as "spined lizard".
A **spinet** is a musical instrument that looks a bit like a piano or a harpsichord. Its name comes from the shape of the thorn-like quills that pluck the strings.
A **spinney** is a small thicket of thorny trees.

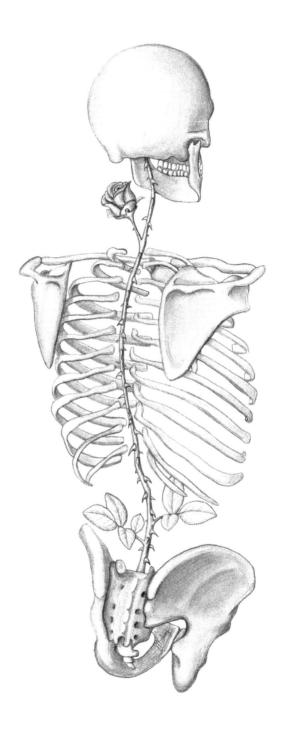

THE STERNUM

The breastbone, technically known as the sternum, is the bone that links your ribs together in the front of your chest. It provides protection for the heart and major blood vessels. The word *sternum* simply means "chest" in Latin, but the parts of the sternum all have names that are sword-related. The sternum is divided into three parts: the manubrium, the gladiolus and the xyphoid process.

The *manubrium* is the uppermost part of the sternum, and literally means the "hilt or handle" of the sword.

The body of the sternum is also known as the *gladiolus*, which is a diminutive of the Roman short sword, *gladius*, meaning "little sword".

The lower tip of the sternum is called the xyphoid process, which comes from the Greek *xyphos*, which also means "sword". Another less commonly used name for the xyphoid process is the ensiform cartilage, which means "sword-shaped" in Latin. Both *ensis* and *gladius* were Latin words for sword.

Fractures of the sternum are often associated with a high mortality rate because a blow powerful enough to break the sternum is usually powerful enough to damage the underlying heart, lungs or major blood vessels.

Related words

The swordfish's scientific name is **Xiphias gladius**, or "sword sword".

The scientific name of the molluscs known as razor shells is **ensis**, because they are as sharp as a sword.

For those who are interested in astronomy, the **ensis** is the name of the group of stars that make up Orion's scabbard or sword sheath.

There is a flower called a **gladiolus** that, before the flowers bloom, looks a little like a sword. It is sometimes called the sword lily.

Gladius is yet another word the Romans used to refer to the penis.

A **sternotomy** is when surgeons saw the sternum in two lengthways using a kind of jigsaw to gain access to the heart and large blood vessels.

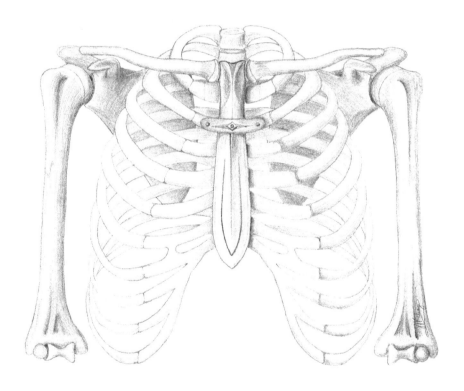

STYLOID PROCESSES

There are at least six styloid processes in the human body: a radial styloid process and an ulnar styloid process in each wrist and a very spiky temporal styloid process at the base of the skull below each ear. Styloid processes serve as anchors for tendons and ligaments. The word "styloid" comes from the Greek *stylos*, meaning a "pillar".

The radial styloid process is located on the thumb side of the wrist, and serves as an anchor for the tendon of the brachioradialis muscle, otherwise known as the "beer drinker's muscle" because it flexes the elbow when the hand is in a can-holding position. As mentioned in the chapter on the radius, a broken radial styloid process is called a chauffeur's fracture. Chauffeurs used to start their cars by hand with a crank, and sometimes the engine would backfire, resulting in painful consequences. The ulnar styloid process is to be found on the other side of the wrist, and serves as an anchor for the ulnar collateral ligament of the wrist. In the illustration, the radial styloid process is the column on the left and the ulnar styloid process is the one on the right.

The temporal styloid process that is located at the base of the skull near the mastoid process is a sharp bony spike that serves as an anchor for three muscles and two ligaments. In a condition called Eagle's syndrome, the temporal styloid process becomes elongated and causes pain when swallowing, turning the head and sticking out the tongue.

(Un)related words

A **stylus** is a small pillar-shaped instrument for writing. However, the English word "stylus" actually comes from the Latin *stilus*, meaning a "stake", a sharp wooden object. The spelling with a –y comes from an erroneous connection with the Greek word for pillar. The word "style" was first used to refer to the mode of expression of an author (someone who writes with a stylus). The word came to mean any other characteristic mode of expression, be it through dressing in stylish clothes or painting in a certain style. The only connection with pillars is the erroneous spelling referred to earlier.

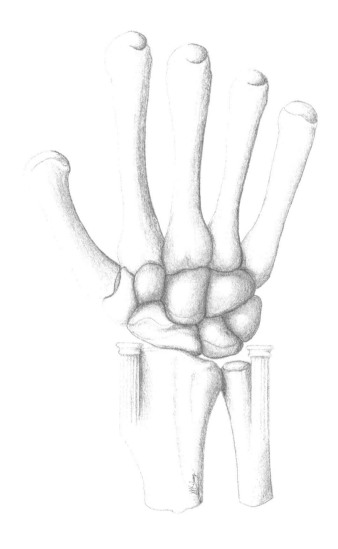

SUTURES

Cranial sutures are where the bones of the skull meet. In Latin a *sutura* was any kind of seam, from the Latin *suere*, which means "to sew".

After the age of two, the bones of the human skull gradually fuse together to form the hard casing that protects our brain. Before then however, the bones of the skull are joined together by an elastic tissue that allows the brain to grow as much as it likes. During childbirth, the sutures allow the baby's skull to be more flexible, making it easier for the head to fit through the birth canal.

In a condition called craniosynostosis, the sutures close (fuse together) too early. The brain however continues to grow. This causes the head to become deformed and the pressure inside the head to gradually increase. Surgeons elegantly treat this condition by peeling back the scalp, chopping out the fused bits (being careful all the while not to damage the brain), and then sewing it all back together again.

The word "suture" also refers to the surgical act of stitching up a wound or incision. The history of surgical suturing is fascinating. One of the oldest ways of sewing up a wound is to use giant ants. All you need to do is pinch the two edges of the wound together, choose an ant of the genus *Oecophylla smaragdina* or *Eciton burchelli*, and hold it close to the wound. It will then bite into the skin on either side of the wound, holding the two parts firmly together. To prevent the ant from letting go, you simply decapitate it.

Romans would sometimes use *fibulae*, small safety pins, to keep the edges of the wound in close proximity. The fibula is also a bone that runs alongside the shinbone, and is named after the Roman safety pin or brooch because it is long and thin and needle-like, especially in birds.

Surgeons have been sewing people up with a needle and thread for hundreds if not thousands of years. Over the centuries, surgical threads have been made from things such as flax, hemp, cotton, gold wire, horse's hair, arteries, nerves, kangaroo tendons, silk and catgut.

Nowadays, surgeons are spoilt for choice and have a long list of options available to them for closing wounds. They can sew a wound using surgical silk or nylon, or they can staple the edges of the wound together, or glue them together using tissue adhesives, or even weld them together using a laser.

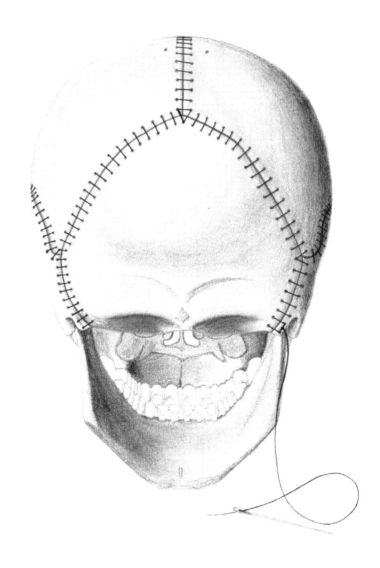

SYNOVIAL FLUID

Eggs are not connected specifically with the shoulder joint, as the picture suggests, but with all synovial joints in the body. There are three types of joints in the human body: fibrous joints, cartilaginous joints and synovial joints.

Fibrous joints more or less completely fuse one structure to another. Cranial sutures, gomphoses (where teeth fit into their sockets) and syndesmoses (the joint between the tibia and fibula in the leg for instance) are all fibrous joints.

Cartilaginous joints are mobile but do not allow for much movement at all. The intervertebral discs that join two vertebra together are a kind of cartilaginous joint called a symphysis.

Synovial joints are what we usually tend to think of as joints: the elbow joint, the hip joint, the finger joints, the shoulder joint, the ankle joint, etc. These joints are called "synovial" joints because they contain synovial fluid, a substance that lubricates the joint and nourishes the cartilage at the end of each adjoining bone. This fluid has a similar colour and consistency to egg white, hence the word "synovial", that comes from the Latin *syn* meaning "like" and *ovum* meaning "egg". Synovial fluid is contained in a bag called a capsule that encapsulates the joint, a bit like the rubber boot around a car's CV joint that keeps the grease in and the dirt out, allowing it to pivot freely.

There are of course other types of joints (nightclubs, prisons and recreational drugs), but which we need not go into here.

Related words

Most words that begin with "syn" or "sym" share the same prefix that means "like" or "same" or "together". For example, a **synonym** is a word with a similar meaning, a **symphony** is a group of instruments that are played together.
The Latin word for "egg", *ovum*, has given us words such as **oval** (egg-shaped), **oviparous** (egg-laying), **ovectomy** (the surgical removal of eggs), and the brand name **Ovaltine**™ (which was originally known as **Ovomaltine**, and was made from egg and malt).

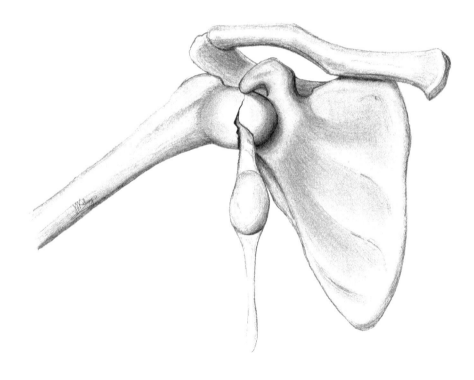

THE TALUS

The word "talus" comes from the Latin *taxillus*, meaning a die, as Roman soldiers would carve their dice from the ankle bones of horses. Another word for the talus which has fallen into disuse was "astragalus", from the Greek *astragalos*, also meaning "a die". Before being used for the ankle bone, *astragalus* designated the first cervical vertebra, atlas, because Greek soldiers would carve their dice from the cervical vertebrae of sheep.

The talus is the anklebone that sits atop the calcaneus (the heel bone) and is supported by a little bony ledge that juts out from the calcaneus called the *sustentaculum tali*, literally "the little prop that supports the talus". The talus is exceptional because while most bones serve as anchors for muscles to attach to, the talus is the largest bone in the human body to which no muscles attach at all.

The word "ankle" is also intriguing. It comes from the same root as "angle", since it is the joint that forms the angle between the leg and the foot. The same root gave us "anglers", people who fish with hooks that are bent at an angle, and "English", descendants of the Angles, fishermen who lived on an area of land that forms an angle between northern Germany and southern Denmark.

Related words

The claws of a bird of prey are known as **talons**, and share their etymology with *talus*.
Hermes' winged sandals are called **talaria** because they have winged heels.
Astragalomancy is the art of divination using dice.
There is a genus of plants called ***astragalus***, but the connection with ankle bones is unclear. Some suggest that the flowers look like the cleft hooves of goats, or maybe the flower clusters look like vertebrae.

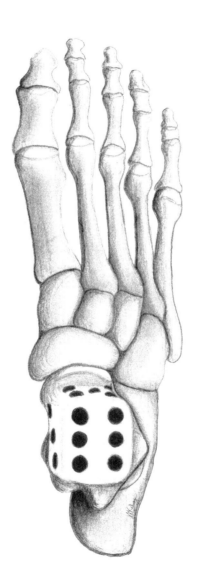

THE TEMPORAL BONE

We have two temporal bones, one on either side of our head. They are the bones that make up the side of the skull around the ears. The name "temporal" has an uncertain origin, but the theories that etymologists have come up with to explain the name are all rather interesting.

Some claim that "temporal" may come from the Latin word *tempus* meaning "time", as in the expression *"tempus fugit"* (or "time flies", as the old lady said as she threw the clock out of the window). The theory is that the hairs that grow in the area of the temporal bone are the first to go grey with age, and are thus markers of the passage of time. The relationship with time could also be explained by the fact that the heart can be felt beating in this area, ticking away like a clock.

Another theory states that "temporal" comes from the Greek word *temnion*, meaning "to wound in battle". The reasoning is that this part of the skull is very thin and can be easily shattered by a blow from an enemy's weapon.

The temporal bone is a very good contender for the title of Most Complicated Bone in the Human Body, and can probably boast the longest list of interestingly-named features. The zygomatic process, mastoid process, bony labyrinth, petrous bone, squamous bone and cochlea, many of which have their own chapters in this book, are all parts of the temporal bone.

Related words

Something **temporary** only lasts a short time.
Contemporary things exist at the same time or come from the same period in time.
A **tempest** is a violent storm. Many languages use the same word for "weather" and for "time", like **"temps"** in French and **"tiempo"** in Spanish for example.
"**Tempo**" means time in Italian, and of course in music refers to the rhythm of a song.

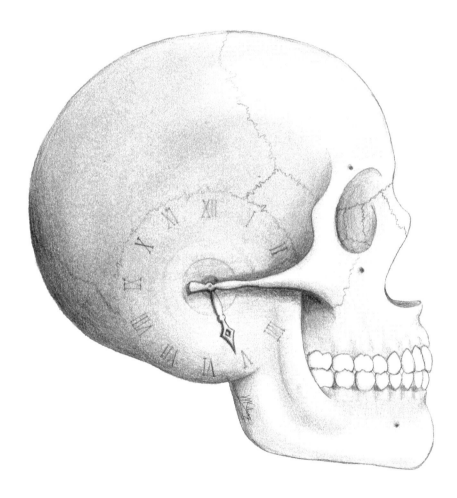

THE THYROID CARTILAGE

The thyroid cartilage is another structure that is related to weaponry and warfare, like the parts of the sternum and the phalanges. *Thyroid* literally means "shield-shaped" in Greek.

The ridge in the middle of the shield is the laryngeal prominence, better known as the Adam's apple. The thyroid cartilage literally serves as a shield to protect the vocal cords, which lie directly behind it. It also serves an anchor for muscles like the thyrohyoid (that goes up from the thyroid cartilage to the hyoid bone) and the sternothyroid (that stretches down from the thyroid cartilage to the sternum). These muscles are involved in swallowing and speech.

The thyroid cartilage sits above the thyroid gland, the lumpy thing in the illustration. The thyroid gland secretes several hormones involved in growth, protein synthesis and calcium regulation. In order to function properly, the thyroid gland requires sufficient amounts of iodine. Natural sources of iodine include marine animals, dairy produce and vegetables grown in iodine rich soil.

Iodine deficiency can cause goitre, a condition where the thyroid gland swells to several times its size, producing a large swelling on the front of the neck. Iodine-deficient pregnant women can give birth to thyroid hormone deficient babies, which stunts their physical and intellectual development. In the past, people who grew up with thyroid hormone deficiency and who were physically deformed and intellectually deficient as a result, were known as cretins. In many countries, iodine has been systematically added to table salt for several decades to avoid iodine deficiency. In places where salt is not systematically iodized, iodine deficiency is still an important public health issue, affecting over two billion people worldwide.

Iodine tablets are also handed out in areas affected by nuclear accidents. The aim of this is to saturate the thyroid gland with normal iodine before it has chance to absorb the radioactive iodine produced by nuclear fission that would cause thyroid cancer. Incidentally, *cancer* means "crab" in Latin, because the large veins that supply tumours resemble a crab's legs.

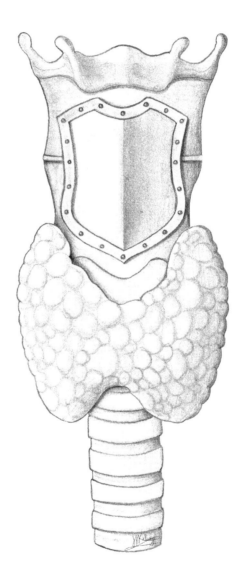

The Tibia

The origin of the word "tibia" is slightly blurred, as we do not know whether the bone got its name from a musical instrument, or whether a musical instrument got its name from the bone. Indeed, in Latin, *tibia* was both the word for the shinbone and the word for a kind of flute or pipe. This is because flutes were often made from the hollow shinbones of animals, just as spades were made from their flat scapulae.

The tibia is one of the most commonly fractured bones in the body. Different kinds of tibial fracture have earned names such as boot top fractures, bumper fractures and toddler fractures. Boot top fractures are breaks that often occur when skiing, right at the top of the ski boot. Bumper fractures are often caused by the bumper of a car striking the outside of a passing pedestrian's tibia. Toddler fractures are spiral fractures often sustained by young children who, lacking the motor skills of most other mammals, often lose their footing on uneven surfaces.

Runners are particularly susceptible to a condition that affects the tibia called shin splints, otherwise known as tibial periostitis, or medial tibial stress syndrome. In this condition, the structures that surround the tibia (the periosteum, the tendons, the bone itself) become inflamed and cause pain due to repetitive stress. The risk of developing shin splints is thought to be increased by running on hard surfaces in thin-soled shoes.

The tibia is the second longest bone in the human body after the femur, or thighbone. Sometimes, one tibia can be shorter than the other, resulting in a limb length discrepancy. Surgeons can lengthen a tibia by about 5 cm by cutting the bone in two and gradually separating the two halves. As the two halves are pulled further and further apart, the bone will keep on growing to try to fill the gap between the two pieces.

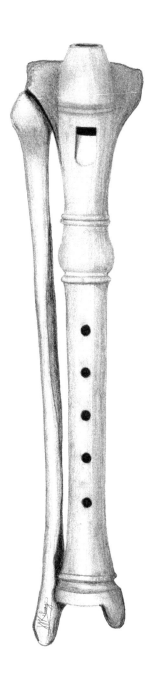

TRABECULAR BONE

We have already talked about bone's outermost layer, known as cortical bone, literally "the bark of the bone". In trees, beneath the bark you will find wood that needs to be dried, cut, planed and sanded before being used by carpenters for building houses. Beneath the bark of the bone however, you will find ready-made beams, or trabeculae, that distribute the forces applied to the bone just as the beams of a house distribute the weight of the roof. The word *trabeculae* means "little beams" in Latin.

Osteopenia and osteoporosis occur when the trabeculae become thinner and weaker, making the bone much more susceptible to fractures. Osteopenia is a mild form of osteoporosis.

Osteopetrosis on the other hand is the opposite condition, in which the bones become harder and denser over time. Osteopetrosis literally means "stone bone", and the condition is also known as Marble Bone Disease.

One of the great mysteries of nature is how woodpeckers avoid brain damage and head injuries. They peck about twelve thousand times a day and with each peck, their head decelerates from about 25 to 0 kilometres per hour instantly. The trabecular bone of their skulls could provide part of the answer. Their trabeculae are plate-like rather than rod-like as in most other animals, which could help them to resist knocking themselves out with every peck. Perhaps a similar adaptation might be seen in head-bangers in a few hundred thousand years when natural selection has done its business.

Bones are not the only organs that contain trabeculae: the penis has them and so do the spleen, the thymus and lymph nodes. The heart has *trabeculae carneae*, literally "fleshy beams". The eyes have a trabecular meshwork than helps drain the aqueous humour from the eye. This drainage system is impaired in people with glaucoma, resulting in increased pressure within the eye. One possible treatment for glaucoma is trabeculectomy, the surgical removal of the trabecular meshwork.

Related words

Trave is an architectural term for a crossbeam.
Trabeculae is the diminutive of *trabs*, meaning beam. In Latin, *trabs* was also a slang term for the penis.

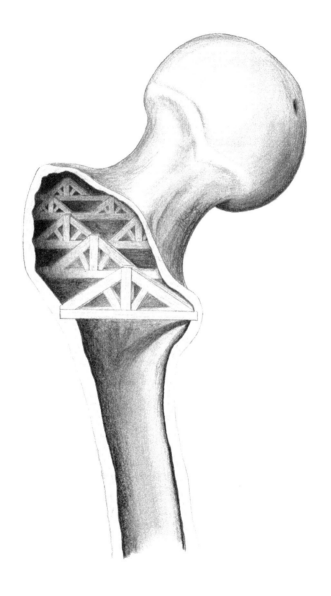

THE TRAGUS

The tragus is one of the many places that the ear can be pierced. It is the small flap of cartilage in front of the ear hole that is covered in downy hair. This hair gradually gets thicker and longer and darker as we age, especially in men, who sometimes end up with more hair on their ears than on top of their heads. The Greeks thought that this little tuft of hair resembled the beard of a goat, and named the structure it grew on *tragos*, meaning "goat" in Greek.

Many people pluck or shave their goat's beard in the interests of aesthetics. Some people even go to the extreme of having their ear hair surgically removed in a process called "tragal flap hair depilation". However, this surgical procedure appears to be of no interest to Anthony Victor, the Indian man who currently holds the World record for longest ear hair, measured at 18.1 cm.

The tragus is only one of the interestingly named features of the outer ear. As mentioned before, the outer-ear itself is actually called the *pinna*, meaning "fin or feather". The lip of cartilage around the edge of the ear is called the helix (meaning "coil or screw"). There is also an anti-helix, an anti-tragus, a scaphoid fossa (a "boat-shaped" depression) and a concha (a "shell").

Related words

Tragedies are plays that depict human suffering and result in an unhappy ending. The word "tragedy" is thought to come from *tragodia*, literally meaning "goat song". The connection between sorrowful dramas and bovines is an uncertain one. Some scholars think that goats were sacrificed during theatre festivals, others think that goats were a prize for the best play, and yet others think that the connection lies in the fact that actors sometimes dressed in goatskins.

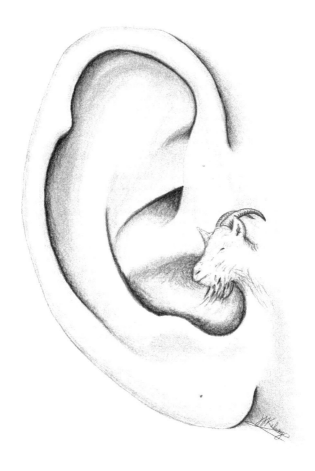

THE TROCHLEA

Our eyes can swivel in all directions thanks to a group of six muscles in each eye. These muscles are anchored to your eyeball and pull on it in order to direct your gaze. One of these muscles, the superior oblique muscle, is unlike the other five because before attaching to the surface of the eyeball, its tendon loops through a pulley made of cartilage called the trochlea. *Trochlea* is Latin for "pulley". The superior oblique muscle of the eye is innervated by the trochlear nerve, named after this extraordinary piece of biological machinery. It seems that another name for this muscle used to be the *amatorius musculus*, the lover's muscle, because it "moves the eye obliquely, giving that cast of the eye call'd ogling", according to Benedict Duddell in his book *Prosodia Chirurgica*, published in 1732.

There is also a trochlea at the distal end of the humerus, in the elbow. It is a structure that looks like the groove in the wheel of a pulley. There is another trochlea in the knee, the groove in which the kneecap slides up and down.

The Latin word *trochlea* comes from the Greek term *trochos*, meaning "wheel". The word "trochanter" also comes from *trochos*, and was originally used by the Greeks to designate the round head of the femur. The word gradually acquired its current meaning, that is to say the bony tubercle at the top of the femur that hurts when you lie on your side on a hard surface.

Related words

A **truckle** is a small wheel or pulley.
A **truck** is a vehicle with wheels that can transport heavy loads, like a pulley.
In geometry, a **trochoid** is the shape described by a point on a rolling wheel. Trochoids, or cycloids as they are sometimes called, look like a series of arches.
A **trochus** is a kind of conical sea snail that looks like a wheel from beneath.
While defenestration is the act of throwing someone out of a window, **infratrochustration** is the act of throwing someone under the wheels of a moving vehicle.

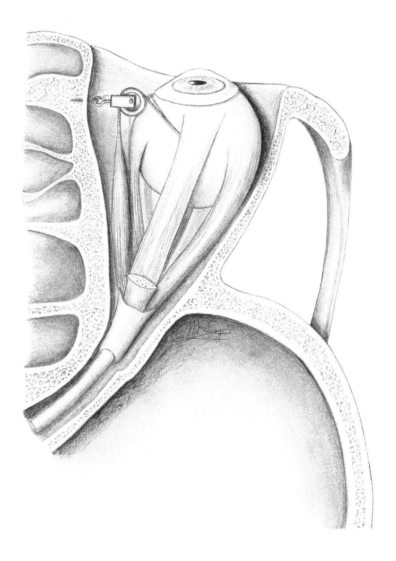

THE TYMPANIC MEMBRANE

We have already discovered two musical structures hidden away in the body, the tibia (the "flute") and the buccinator (the "trumpet player"). The third is the tympanic membrane or tympanum, more commonly known as the eardrum. And that is exactly what "tympanic" means, from the Latin *tympanum*, meaning "drum".

The tympanic membrane is unlike any other drum however, because it works backwards. An ordinary drum is hit with a drumstick, making the drum skin vibrate, and these vibrations create air pressure waves that we call sound. The eardrum works the other way round. Sound waves enter the auditory canal and make the tympanic membrane (the drum skin) vibrate, and these vibrations are then transmitted to the malleus (the drumstick) and the other ossicles, before being sent off to the cochlea to be transformed into electrical signals that are then dispatched to the brain to be interpreted as speech, music or noise.

In order to detect the slightest sound waves, the tympanic membrane needs to be very thin, about a tenth of a millimetre in thickness. Despite its thinness, it is extremely resistant, but can nevertheless be torn by sudden extreme changes in air pressure, like you might experience when flying, diving, or in the blast of an explosion. Eardrums usually heal on their own within six months. The tympanic membrane can also be punctured on purpose (a surgical procedure known as tympanotomy) to allow pus to drain out of the middle ear in the case of an infection.

Related words

The Latin word *tympanum* comes from the Greek *tympanon*, which itself comes from the verb *typtein*, meaning "to strike, to beat". This verb gave *typos*, meaning "an impression, a mark, or a symbol". All of the English words that contain the suffix "-type" come from this same root, like **stereotype**, **archetype**, **phenotype**, **prototype**, as well as the verb "to type".

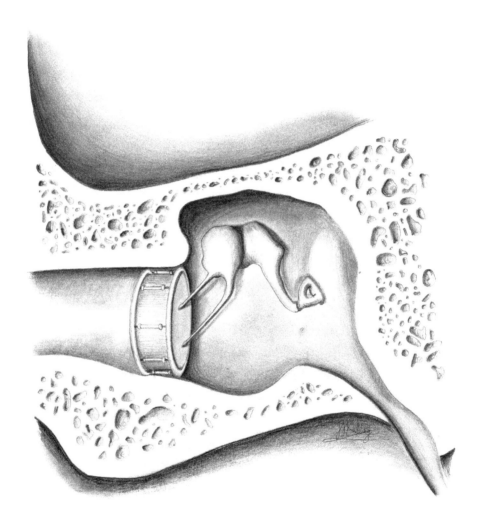

THE UVULA

The technical term for the uvula is "the dangly thing" at the back of the throat. If you feel the roof of your mouth with your tongue, starting just behind the front teeth, you will first feel the bony hard palate, then the soft palate, and then, if you have a very mobile tongue, the uvula, which is in fact an extension of the soft palate. In Latin, *uvula* is the diminutive of *uva*, and means "the little grape".

The uvula has several useful functions. When you swallow, the soft palate and the uvula move upwards to block off the nasopharynx to avoid food going into the nose. If touched, the uvula will induce the gag reflex, which is useful to prevent you from choking if you start to swallow something too large that has not been chewed enough. The uvula also secretes saliva, which is thought to lubricate the back of the throat and the vocal cords. People who snore a lot tend to have enlarged uvulae, and this is thought to contribute to sleep apnoea. One possible treatment for this is uvulopalatopharyngoplasty which involves the removal of the uvula. This can cause a dry throat and something known as "velopharyngeal insufficiency". When you pronounce letters like -p, -t, -k, -b, -d and -g (known as "plosive" letters) the soft palate and uvula close off the nasal passage so that pressure can build up to be released explosively. In velopharyngeal insufficiency, the nasal passage is not properly blocked off and air leaks out of the nose, making plosive letters sound like nasal letters (-b sounds like -m for instance).

Related words

The uvea, one of the three layers of the eye, is another piece of anatomy named after a grape. When the white sclera is peeled away, the dark red uvea is exposed, making the eye look like a large red grape.

Grapes are in fact a type of berry, and we have more berries in the lungs. An *acinus* ("berry" in Latin) is a bunch of alveoli at the end of a bronchiole (a bunch of little air sacs at the end of a tiny tube), that looks like a raspberry on its stalk or a bunch of grapes.

"Uva" still means "grape" in several Latin languages such as Italian, Spanish and Portuguese.

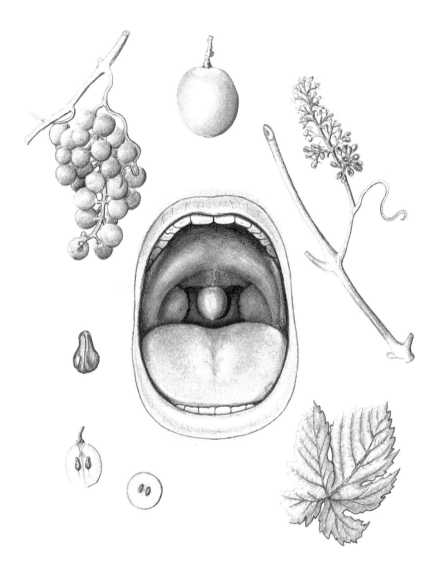

THE VAGINA

We have already mentioned a few of the slang terms for penis used by Latin speakers: *trabs* ("beam"), *cauda* ("tail") and *gladius* ("sword"). The vagina is the muscular tube into which the gladius is introduced during sexual intercourse. In Latin, a *vagina* is a "scabbard or sheath" for a sword.

Research has shown that only about fifty percent of people are able to correctly label a diagram of the visible female genitalia and reproductive organs. Surprisingly, women are not much better at it than men. The vulva is another name for the external female genitalia. This includes everything you can see from outside: the labia minora and majora ("the greater and lesser lips"), the mons pubis ("the pubic mound"), the vaginal opening and the urinary meatus that both open into the vulval vestibule, the clitoris (the "hillock"), the hymen ("the membrane") and a few other less well-known structures. The vagina is the muscular tube that links the vulva to the cervix (the "neck") of the uterus.

The uterus, otherwise known as the womb, has a curious history. Ancient Egyptians and Greeks believed that hysteria was caused by the uterus wandering about the body and interfering with other organs. The word "hysteria" actually comes from the Greek word for uterus, *hystera* (a root found in modern medical words like hysterectomy and hysteroscopy). The best way to treat hysteria was to lure the wandering uterus back down to its correct, pelvic position. Presenting the vulva with pleasant smelling substances would entice the uterus back down, whereas smelling foetid substances would drive the uterus away from the upper parts of the body. Even today, many women do not really know where their uterus is or what it does, so perhaps ancient doctors can be excused for these misunderstandings.

Surprisingly, women are not the only ones with vaginas. Both men and women have them at the bottom of their skull. Well, not exactly vaginas, but the base of the temporal styloid processes are enclosed in a bony sheath called a vaginal process.

Related words

The word "vanilla" is derived from the Latin *vagina*, and literally means a "little pod" (*i.e.* a sheath for seeds).

Invaginations are formed by a surface that is folded in on itself, like the surface of a balloon when you poke your finger into it.

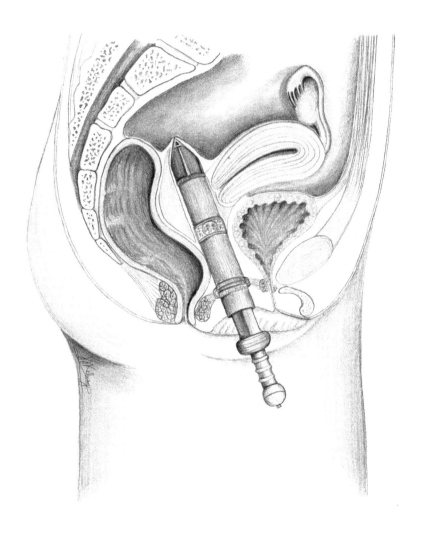

THE VERMIS

The *cerebellum* (which means "little brain" in Latin), is part of the central nervous system. It is involved in balance and movement coordination amongst many other things. Like the brain, the cerebellum is composed of two hemispheres, but whereas the brain's two hemispheres are divided by the *falx cerebri*, the cerebellum's hemispheres are divided by the *vermis*. The word *vermis* means "worm" in Latin. We appear to be infested by worms, since we have at least eighteen in total: eight lumbrical muscles in the hands, eight in the feet, a vermis and a vermiform appendix. If you thought that Donald Trump was the only one with a worm in his brain, you were wrong. Sadly, his is a real one.

In "Dandy Walker" syndrome, the vermis is absent or extremely small. It is not called Dandy Walker syndrome because people with this syndrome walk like dandies (the cerebellum is particularly important in walking after all), but it is named after the two American neurosurgeons who first described the condition. It is a genetic disorder that can lead to intellectual disability, hydrocephalus (an accumulation of fluid in the skull), seizures and many other symptoms.

Related words

Vermin include animals that humans dislike, like worms, rodents, insects and snakes.
Vermicelli are the worms made of pasta that you eat.
Vermilion is a bright red dye that was originally made from squashing up little grubs.

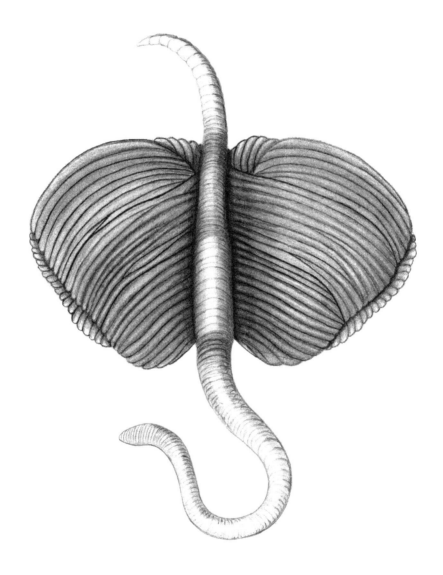

THE VINCULA

Fingers are fascinating things. They are extremely strong for their size, but contain no muscles whatsoever. All of the muscles that move the fingers are in fact in the hands and forearms, and only their tendons reach the actual fingers. The flexor tendons (*i.e.* the tendons of the muscles that bend the fingers) are held close to the finger bones by a system of pulleys at each joint, a bit like the eyes on a fishing rod which allow the fishing line to follow the rod when it bends rather than stretching directly from the reel to the tip of the rod. Some rock climbers are able to hang their entire weight on one or two fingers, putting these pulleys under extreme tension. The pulleys can snap, and the flexor tendons can become detached from the fingertips if the tension is excessive.

The pulleys have been removed in the illustration to reveal the vincula. The vincula are small tendinous bands of connective tissue that anchor the tendons of the finger flexor muscles to the phalanges. The word *vinculum* means a "fetter, chain or bond" in Latin. The vincula also contain small blood vessels that supply the flexor tendons with blood.

Relatively recently, the tendon of the long head of the biceps has been shown to have vincula as well. As discussed in the chapter on the *lacertus fibrosus*, the biceps tendon can break, resulting in a short bulging biceps known as Popeye's sign. Sometimes, even if the biceps tendon snaps, the muscle does not migrate to form the characteristic bulge. This could be because the vincula are still holding onto the tendon, anchoring it in its sheath.

Related Words

You may have heard the Latin word *vincula* before in the name of **Saint Peter ad Vincula**, also known as Saint Peter in Chains. According to the New Testament (the second instalment of the Bible), one of Jesus's twelve apostles, Peter, was imprisoned and chained up for being a follower of Jesus by King Herod Agrippa, who was king of Judea from 41 to 44 AD. Luckily, before he had chance to be executed, a passing angel popped in and miraculously freed him from his chains.

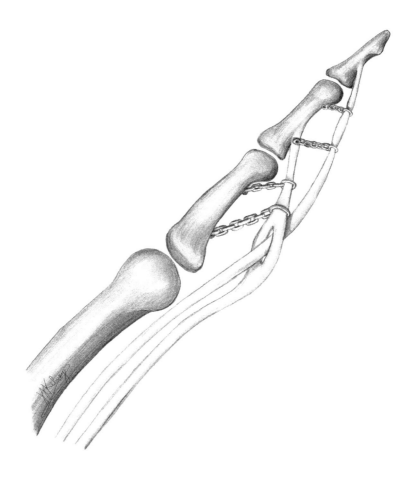

THE ZYGOMATIC ARCH

The zygomatic arch is just one of several references to farmyard equipment in anatomical terminology: there is also the falx cerebri (a sickle or scythe), the molar teeth (millstones) and of course the vomer bone (a ploughshare).

The word "zygomatic" derives from the Greek *zygon* meaning a "yoke" as in the curved piece of wood used to attach two oxen together in order to pull a plough or cart.

The zygomatic arch is the cheekbone that you can feel just in front of the tragus of the ear. Pronounced zygomatic arches, or high cheekbones as they are popularly called, appear to be almost universally valued as an attractive physical trait. However, it is hard to say why this is. Some people believe that high cheekbones are an indicator of sexual maturity. Indeed, children's faces are usually round with full cheeks and barely visible cheekbones. Some studies also suggest that high cheekbones are perceived as a mark of trustworthiness. Others think that large cheekbones and jutting square jaws evolved to be able to withstand the force of a punch (which is a plausible explanation because good-looking people are usually very annoying).

Another term for the zygomatic arch is the malar bone, which is possibly related to the Latin word for apple, *malum*. This could be because flushed cheeks are a similar colour to ripe red apples.

Related Words

Since yokes are used to bind two things together, the term "**zygote**" is used to refer to the union of a sperm cell (a spermatozoon) and an egg cell (an ovum). The zygote is at first a single cell. During a process known as cleavage, this cell divides into 2, then into 4, then into 8, then into 16. At this stage, the zygote is called a *morula*, Latin for "mulberry". The morula divides again and becomes a blastocyst, which in turn becomes an embryo.

Veins usually come in pairs, one on the left hand side of the body and one on the right. The **azygos** vein however is present only on the right hand side, hence its name. It has no similar vein on the left hand side for it to be yoked to.

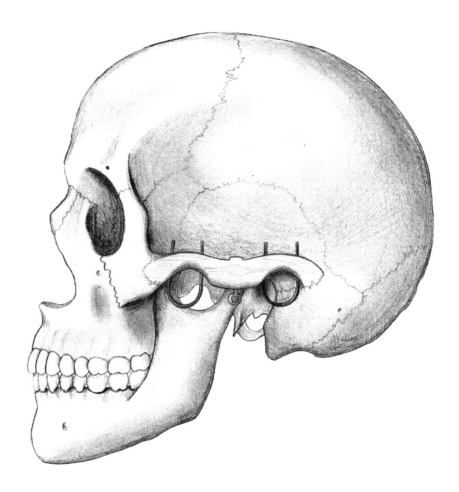

APPENDIX

This appendix contains all of the anatomical terms mentioned throughout this book, as well as many more. It does not include all anatomical terms, but lists the ones with the most interesting or unexpected origins. I chose not to illustrate these either because the illustration would have been too abstract, too boring or, more often, too difficult to draw. If you do not know where these body parts are, or what their function is, you can find a seemingly unlimited amount of information on the internet.

A

acetabulum: a little vinegar cup
acinus: berry
acromion: the summit of the shoulder
ala: wings
alveolus: a small socket, a hollow cavity, the cell of a honeycomb
ampulla: a vase or amphora
amygdala: an almond
ankle: an angle
antrum: a cave
anus, **annulus**: a ring
aorta: to raise, to lift, to hang
appendix: hanging from

arachnoid: spider-like
arcuate: arched
artery: perhaps a pipe that holds air
arytenoid: jug-shaped or ladle-shaped
astragalus: dice
astrocyte: a star cell
atlas: the Titan who holds up the celestial orb
atrium: the central room of a Roman house
auricle, auricula: ear
axon: the axis of a neuron
azygos: not yoked (uncoupled, alone)

B

biceps: two heads
blastula: a germ or bud

buccinator: a trumpet player
bursa: a pouch

C

caecum: blind
calyx, calices: a husk, a cup
cancer: a crab
canine teeth: dog's teeth
capillary: head hair
capitate (and capitis, capitellum, capitulum, etc.): a head
carotid: stupefy (blood choke by carotid compression)
cauda equina: a horse's tail
cava: hollow, like a cave
celiac: of the belly
cervix: the neck
chiasma: crossed-over, like the Greek letter khi (χ)
clavicle: a little key

clitoris: perhaps hillock, key, tickle, touch lasciviously
coccyx: a cuckoo
cochlea: a snail shell
collagen: that produces glue
concha: a shell
condyle: a knuckle
coracoid: crow shaped
cornea: horny
coronoid, coronary: crown shaped
cortex: bark
cremaster: hanging
cribriform: sieve-like
cricoid: a ring
crista galli: a cockscombe
cuneiform: wedge shaped

D

dartos: flogged, skinned or flayed
deltoid: shaped like the Greek capital letter delta (Δ)
detrusor: to thrust, to drive out
diaphragm: a wall across the thorax

digastric: two-bellied
ductus deferens: the canal that carries away
duodenum: twelve fingers
dura mater: the hard mother

E

ethmoid: sieve-shaped

erythrocyte: a red cell

F

fabella: a bean, a fava
falx cerebri: the sickle or scythe of the brain
falciform: shaped like a scythe or sickle
fascia: a band or bandage
femur: perhaps from the Latin verb *fero*, meaning "I bear"
fenestra: window

fibula: a brooch or safety pin (the same as *peroneus* in Greek)
fimbria: a fringe
finger: from *fingro*, five
follicle: a little bag
fontanelle: a spring or fountain
fornix: an arch or vault
fossa: a trench, a ditch
fovea: a pit

G

ganglion: a swelling
gastrocnemius: the belly of the leg
gemellus: twin
geniculate: bent like a knee
glabella: smooth, hairless
gladius, gladiolus: a Roman short sword
gland: an acorn
glans penis: the acorn of the penis

glenoid: mirror-like or pupil like
glomerulus: a small ball of yarn
gluteus: the buttock
gonad: a seed
gracilis: thin or slender
gubernaculum: a helm
gyrus: a circle

H

hallux: to leap, to jump
hamate, hamulus: a fishing hook
helix: a coil or screw
hippocampus: a sea-horse

humerus: from the Greek *omos* meaning shoulder

I

ilium, ileum: the flank, the entrails
incus: an anvil
index: to point

inguinal: the groin
iris: the Greek godess of rainbows

J

jejunum: empty, fasting

K

kyphosis: bent or bowed

L

labrum, labium: a lip
labyrinth: a maze
lacertus fibrosus: a fibrous lizard
lacrimal bone: the tear bone

lamina: a thin sheet of material
lemniscus: a band
lens: lentil
lenticular: lentil-shaped

ligament: to tie, to attach, to link
linea alba: a white line
linea aspera: a rough line
lingual: little tongue

lumbar: relating to the loins
lumbricals: worms
lunatum: half-moon shaped

M

malleolus: little hammer
malleus: hammer
mastoid: breast-like
medulla: marrow
meniscus: crescent moon shaped

metacarpus: beyond the wrist
mitral: shaped like a pope's mitre
molar: a millstone
muscle: little mouse
myelin: marrow

N

navicular: shaped like a little boat
neuron: a string or rope

node: a knot

O

obturator: a plug, a stopper
odontoid: tooth shaped
oesophagus: the gullet, to carry food

olecranon: the head of the elbow
ostium: a door, an opening

P

pampiniform: tendril-shaped, vine-like
panniculus: a little covering
papilla: a nipple
parietal: a wall
parotid: near the ear (nothing to do with parrots disappointingly)
patella: a little plate or dish
pectineus, pectinate: a comb
pedicle: a little foot or the stalk of a fruit
pelvis: a wide bowl or basin
pennate: feather-like
peroneus: a brooch or safety pin (the same as *fibula* in Latin)
pes anserinus: the goose's foot
petrous, petrosal: stone-like
phalanx: a Greek military formation, a line of battle
physis (as in diaphysis): growth
pia mater: the kind mother

pineal: a pine nut
piriformis: pear-shaped
pisiform: pea-shaped
pituitary: phlegm, slime, mucus
platysma: a plate
plexus: a braid or plait
pollex: from *polleo*, "I am strong"
pons: a bridge
popliteal: relating to the back of the knee
porta, portal: a gate
promontory: a raised projection of land
pterygoid: wing-shaped
pudendal: shameful, to be ashamed of
pulvinar: pillow
pupil: a little doll
pylorus: a gatekeeper
pyramidalis: pyramid-shaped

Q

quadratus: square

quadriceps: four heads

R

radius: a spoke, a staff, a ray of light
ramus: a branch
ranine: frog-like
retina: a casting net, a fishing net

retinaculum: to restrain, to tether
rhomboid: a parallelogram
risorius: one who laughs

S

saccule: a little bag
sacrum: a sacred, holy bone

salpinx: a trumpet
saphenous: hidden

sartorius: a tailor
scala: a staircase
scalene: unequal
scaphoid: boat-shaped
scapula: a spade, a shovel
sclera: hard
septum: hedge or fence
serratus: a saw blade
sesamoid: sesame seed shaped
sigmoid: shaped like the Greek letter sigma (ς)
skeleton: dried up
soleus: a flatfish, a sole
soma: the body

sphenoid: wedge-shaped (or perhaps from *sphecoid*, "wasp-like")
spine: thorny
splenius: a bandage
squamous: fish-scales
stapes: a stirrup
styloid: shaped like a column or a pillar
sulcus: a furrow
sustentaculum: a prop or support
suture: a seam
synapse: a conjunction
synovial: egg-like

T

talus: a dice
tarsus: flat wickerwork mat used for drying things on
tectum: roof
temporal: related to time (or perhaps "to wound in battle")
tentorium: tent
thalamus: inner chamber, bridal chamber or bed
thenar: to strike (Greek *thenein*)

thyroid: shield-shaped
tibia: a flute or pipe
trabeculae: beams
tragus: a goat
triceps: three heads
trochanter: a wheel (Greek *trochos*)
trochlea: a pulley
tympanum: a drum

U

uncus: a hook
utricle: a little bag

uvula: a grape

V

vagina: a scabbard or sheath
vagus: wandering
vertebra: from *vetere*, "to turn"
vestibule: an antechamber, an entrance, a lobby
vermiform: worm-shaped

vermis: a worm
vincula: a chain
vitreous: glassy
vomer: a ploughshare

X

xyphoid: sword-like

Z

zonula: small belt or girdle

zygomatic: a yoke for pairing oxen

Greek Letters

Capital	Lower Case	English Name	Example
A	α	Alpha	--
B	β	Beta	--
Γ	γ	Gamma	--
Δ	δ	Delta	The **deltoid muscle** is a triangular muscle of the shoulder that looks like the capital letter delta.
E	ε	Epsilon	--
Z	ζ	Zeta	--
H	η	Eta	--
Θ	θ	Theta	--
I	ι	Iota	--
K	κ	Kappa	--
Λ	λ	Lambda	The **lambdoid suture** is where the occipital and parietal bones of the skull.
M	μ	Mu	--
N	ν	Nu	--
Ξ	ξ	Xi	--
O	ο	Omicron	--
Π	π	Pi	--
P	ρ	Rho	--
Σ	σ/ς	Sigma	Part of the large intestine is called the **sigmoid colon**. **Sigmoid sinuses** are large veins in the skull. Both are shaped roughly sigma-shaped.
T	τ	Tau	--
Y	υ	Upsilon	The **hyoid bone** is an upsilon-shaped bone in the neck that, if broken, suggests strangulation.
Φ	φ	Phi	--
X	χ	Khi	The **optical chiasma** is where the two optical nerves cross over like the two branches of the Greek letter khi.
Ψ	ψ	Psi	--
Ω	ω	Omega	--

Greek letters are used extensively in biology and physiology, but not so much in anatomy. There are for instance *alpha*, *beta* and *gamma* motor neurons. Brain waves are classed according to their frequency into *alpha*, *beta*, *gamma*, *delta*, *theta* and *mu* waves. Our cells contain so many types of DNA polymerase (proteins that repair DNA) that practically all of the letters of the Greek alphabet have been used up in naming them. The accumulation of *tau* proteins in the brain is involved in Alzheimer's Disease. Our cell membranes contain *omega*-3 and *omega*-6 fatty acids.

NUMBERS

Number	Latin prefix	Greek prefix	Example
1	*uni*	*mono*	--
2	*du* *bi*	*di* *duo*	The **biceps** is a muscle with two heads. The **digastric** muscle is a muscle with two bellies.
3	*tri*	*tri*	The **triceps** is a muscle with three heads. We have a triceps brachii in the arm and a triceps surae in the calf.
4	*quadri*	*tetra*	The **quadriceps** is a muscle with four heads. **Tetraplegia** is the paralysis of all four limbs.
5	*quinque*	*penta*	A **pentadactyl** has five fingers. **Quintus digitus** is the Latin name for the fifth digit of the hands and feet (the little fingers and the little toes).
6	*sexa*	*hexa*	--
7	*septi*	*hepta*	--
8	*octo*	*octo*	--
9	*novem*	*ennea*	--
10	*dec*	*deca*	--
11	*undec*	*hendec*	--
12	*duoden* *duodec*	*dodeca*	The **duodenum** is the first part of the small intestine, which was considered to be 12 finger widths long on average by the anatomists who named it. Originally, in Greek, it was called the **dodecadactylum**.

As with the Greek letters, words based on Greek and Latin numbers are more prevalent in biology than in anatomy. For instance, **mono**zygotic twins come from a single egg. There are as many **uni**cellular organisms like bacteria and fungi in our bodies as there are human cells. We have **uni**polar and **bi**polar neurons. **Tri**acyglycerol is the molecule that men often have too much of around their wastes, and women usually think they have too much of on their thighs and buttocks. **Tetra**chromats are people with four types of photoreceptors in their retinas, as opposed to the usual three. Insects are **hexa**pods because they have six legs, while **octo**puses have eight and **deca**poda (a kind of crustacean) have ten.

GEOMETRIC SHAPES

Shape	Greek or Latin	English	Example
	quadratus	square, rectangle	The **quadratus femoris** and **quadratus pronator** are small rectangular muscles in the buttock and forearm, respectively.
	teres	round and smooth	The **teres minor** and **teres major** muscles are cylindrical shoulder muscles. The **teres pronator** is a muscle in the forearm.
	trapezoid	trapezoid	The **trapezius** is a large muscle in the back. The **trapezium** and **trapezoid** are two of the eight carpal bones of the wrist.
	rhombus	rhombus or diamond	The **rhomboids** are muscles in the upper back that allow you to squeeze your shoulder blades together.
	triquetrum	triangle	The **triquetrum** is one of the eight carpal bones of the wrist.
	skalenos	unequal	There are three **scalene** muscles in the neck: the anterior, posterior and medius. They are of unequal length like the sides of a scalene triangle.
	cuneus *sphen*	wedge	There three **cuneiform** bones in the rear foot. Surprisingly, The **sphenoid** bone in the skull is not at all wedge-shaped.
	cubus	cube	The **cuboid** bone is a roughly cubic bone in the side of the foot.

Colours

Colour	Greek	Latin	English	Example
	leuko	alba	white	The linea alba is the white line that separates a six-pack into two lots of three. Albinism causes white skin and hair. Leucocytes are white blood cells.
	melano	negro	black	The substantia nigra is a structure in the brain that secretes dopamine. Melanin is the dark pigment that colours our skin, hair and iris.
	polio	canus	grey	Poliomyelitis is a disease that affects the grey matter of the central nervous system.
	erythro	ruber	red	Erythrocytes are red blood cells. The nucleus ruber is a group of neurons in the brain stem. Rubella is a disease that causes a red rash.
	xantho cirrho	flavum luteus	yellow	Ligamenta flava bind our vertebrae together. Corpora lutea are found in the ovaries. Xanthemia is yellow blood. Cirrhosis is a yellow liver.
	chloro	viridi	green	Chlorosis, or green sickness, also known as hypochromic anaemia, can make the skin look green. Chlorephidrosis is greenish sweat.
	cyano	cerule	blue	Cyanosis due to low blood oxygen levels makes the lips appear blue. The locus coeruleus is literally a "blue spot" in the brainstem.
	porphyr	purpur	purple	Porphyria is a condition that makes your urine appear purple. Purpura causes purple spots to appear on your skin due to bleeding under the skin.
	chromo	color	colour	Chromosomes are easily stained with artificial colouring to be viewed under a microscope.

REFERENCES

Articles and books

Agrawal, Anuj. 2019. 'Musculoskeletal Etymology: What's in a Name?' *Journal of Clinical Orthopaedics and Trauma* 10 (2): 387–94.

Back, G. W., S. Nadig, S. Uppal, and A. P. Coatesworth. 2004. 'Why Do We Have a Uvula?: Literature Review and a New Theory'. *Clinical Otolaryngology & Allied Sciences* 29 (6): 689–93.

Bagoji, Ishwar B., Gavishiddappa A. Hadimani, Balappa M. Bannur, B. G. Patil, Ambadasu Bharata, M. A. Doshi, and B. S. Patil. 2014. 'An Anatomical Insight on the Supernumerary Head of Biceps Brachii and Its Clinical Relevance–Cadaveric Study'. *Journal of Advanced Scientific Research* 5 (1): 18–21.

Brassett, Cecilia, Emily Evans, and Isla Fay. 2018. *The Secret Language of Anatomy: An Illustrated Guide to the Origins of Anatomical Terms.*

Chmielewski, Piotr Paweł. 2019. 'New Terminologia Anatomica: Cranium and Extracranial Bones of Head'. *Folia Morphologica*, December.

Chugh, Priyamvada, and Ewa K. Paluch. 2018. 'The Actin Cortex at a Glance'. *Journal of Cell Science* 131 (14).

Cole, Thomas. 1991. 'Who Was Corax?' *Illinois Classical Studies* 16 (1/2): 65–84.

Collin, P. H. 2005. *Dictionary of Medical Terms.* London: A & C Black.

Cooper, N., and L. Cascarini. 2008. 'Maxillary Etymologies'. *British Dental Journal* 205 (7): 393–94.

Corriero, Claudia. 2016. 'Medical Terminology, Greek Roots, Latin Roots, Medical Jargon, Pocket'. *Pocket Anatomy* (blog). 21 October 2016.

Dalip, Dominic, Joe Iwanaga, Rod J Oskouian, and R. Shane Tubbs. 2018. 'A Comprehensive Review of the Fabella Bone'. *Cureus*, June.

Das, Sushant Swaroop, Sandeep Saluja, and Neelam Vasudeva. 2017. 'Biometrics of Pyramidalis Muscle and Its Clinical Importance'. *Journal of Clinical and Diagnostic Research : JCDR* 11 (2): AC05–7.

Duddell, Benedict. 1732. *Prosodia Chirurgica; Or, A Memoria Technica: Calculated for the Use of Old Practitioners, as Well as Young Students in Surgery.* Charles Corbett, and Richard Chandler.

Dunglison, Robley. 1846. *A Dictionary of Medical Science: Containing a Concise Account of the Various Subjects and Terms : With the French and Other Synonymes, Notices of Climate, and of Celebrated Mineral Waters, Formulae for Various Officinal and Empirical Preparations, Etc.* Lea Brothers.

Dye, Scott F., B.E. van Dam, and G. Wilbur Westin. 1991. 'Etymology and the Orthopaedic Surgeon: Onomasticon (Vocabulary)'. *The Iowa Orthopaedic Journal* 11: 84–90.

Frixione, Eugenio. 2017. 'What Is in a Word? *Neuron* : Early Usage and Evolution in Antiquity to Its Long-Lasting Current Significance'. *Journal of the History of the Neurosciences* 26 (4): 406–24.

Galbraith, R. Michael, and Mark E. Lavallee. 2009. 'Medial Tibial Stress Syndrome: Conservative Treatment Options'. *Current Reviews in Musculoskeletal Medicine* 2 (3): 127–33.

Goh, Yau H., Ignatius Mark, and Willard E. Fee. 2007. 'Quality of Life 17 to 20 Years after Uvulopalatopharyngoplasty'. *The Laryngoscope* 117 (3): 503–6.

Grob, K., T. Ackland, M. S. Kuster, M. Manestar, and L. Filgueira. 2016. 'A Newly Discovered Muscle: The Tensor of the Vastus Intermedius'. *Clinical Anatomy (New York, N.Y.)* 29 (2): 256–63.

Hall, Ferris M. 2005. 'Of Fractures, Hip and Hangman, of Gamekeepers and Red Herrings'. *RadioGraphics* 25 (2): 367–68.

Haubrich, William S. 2003. *Medical Meanings: A Glossary of Word Origins*. 2nd ed. Philadelphia: American College of Physicians.

Hofman, Jack L. 1980. 'Scapula Skin-Dressing and Fiber-Processing Tools'. *Plains Anthropologist* 25 (88): 135–41.

Joffe, Natalie F. 1948. 'The Vernacular of Menstruation'. WORD 4 (3): 181–86.

Johnson, L. L., B. M. Bays, and G. Eda van Dyk. 1992. 'Vincula of the Biceps Tendon in the Glenohumeral Joint: An Arthroscopic and Anatomic Study'. *Journal of Shoulder and Elbow Surgery* 1 (3): 162–66.

Jones, Edward G. 1985. 'The History of the Thalamus'. In *The Thalamus*, edited by Edward G. Jones, 3–42. Boston, MA: Springer US.

Kaplan, Solomon Alexander. 2007. 'The Pituitary Gland: A Brief History'. *Pituitary* 10 (4): 323–25.

Kircher, K. F. 1987. 'How the Sacrum Got Its Name'. *JAMA: The Journal of the American Medical Association* 258 (3): 325.

Lee, Patrick, Tim B. Hunter, and Mihra Taljanovic. 2004. 'Musculoskeletal Colloquialisms: How Did We Come Up with These Names?' *RadioGraphics* 24 (4): 1009–27.

Lydiatt, Daniel D., and Gregory S. Bucher. 2010. 'The Historical Latin and Etymology of Selected Anatomical Terms of the Larynx'. *Clinical Anatomy*, NA-NA.

Mehta, Lopa A., M. Natrajan, and M. L. Kothari. 1996. 'Understanding Anatomical Terms'. *Clinical Anatomy* 9 (5): 330–36.

Micale, Mark S. 2019. *Approaching Hysteria: Disease and Its Interpretations*. Princeton University Press.

Mohammed, Hussan, Matthew R. Skalski, Dakshesh B. Patel, Anderanik Tomasian, Aaron J. Schein, Eric A. White, George F. Rick Hatch, and George R. Matcuk. 2016. 'Coracoid Process: The Lighthouse of the Shoulder'. *RadioGraphics* 36 (7): 2084–2101.

Musil, Vladimir, Zdenek Suchomel, Petra Malinova, Josef Stingl, Martin Vlcek, and Marek Vacha. 2015. 'The History of Latin Terminology of Human Skeletal Muscles (from Vesalius to the Present)'. *Surgical and Radiologic Anatomy* 37 (1): 33–41.

Neumann, Paul E. 2018. 'What the 'ell? Testicle Is a Diminutive!' *Clinical Anatomy* 31 (8): 1100–1103.

Neumann, Paul E., Robert Baud, and Pierre Sprumont. 2017. 'Ordering by the Numbers in Anatomy and by Letters Too'. *Clinical Anatomy* 30 (6): 700–702.

Ojumah, Naomi, and Marios Loukas. 2018. 'The Intriguing History of the Term Sacrum'. *The Spine Scholar* 2 (1): 17–18.

Paluzzi, Alessandro, Juan Fernandez-Miranda, Matthew Torrenti, and Paul Gardner. 2012. 'Retracing the Etymology of Terms in Neuroanatomy'. *Clinical Anatomy* 25 (8): 1005–14.

Ridley, Lloyd J, Jason Han, William E Ridley, and Hao Xiang. 2018. 'Coracoid and Coronoid: Normal Anatomy'. *Journal of Medical Imaging and Radiation Oncology* 62 (October): 128–29.

Sakai, Tatsuo. 2007. 'Historical Evolution of Anatomical Terminology from Ancient to Modern'. *Anatomical Science International* 82 (2): 65–81.

Sanan, Abhay, and Harry R. van Loveren. 1999. 'The Arachnoid and the Myth of Arachne'. *Neurosurgery* 45 (1): 152–157.

Schiappa, J., and R. Van Hee. 2012. 'From Ants to Staples: History and Ideas Concerning Suturing Techniques'. *Acta Chirurgica Belgica* 112 (5): 395–402. https://doi.org/10.1080/00015458.2012.11680861.

Schwab, I R, and G R O'Connor. 2005. 'The Lonely Eye'. *The British Journal of Ophthalmology* 89 (3): 256.

Serra, Carlo, Lelio Guida, Victor E. Staartjes, Niklaus Krayenbühl, and Uğur Türe. 2019. 'Historical Controversies about the Thalamus: From Etymology to Function'. *Neurosurgical Focus* 47 (3): E13.

Shahar, D. & Sayers, M. G. L. Prominent exostosis projecting from the occipital squama more substantial and prevalent in young adult than older age groups. *Sci. Rep.* 8, 3354 (2018).

Shoja, Mohammadali M., Lauren D. Hoepfner, Paul S. Agutter, Rajani Singh, and R. Shane Tubbs. 2016. 'History of the Pineal Gland'. *Child's Nervous System* 32 (4): 583–86.

Smith, Bromley. 1921. 'Corax and Probability'. *Quarterly Journal of Speech* 7 (1): 13–42.

Stross, Brian. 'The Mesoamerican Sacrum Bone: Doorway to the Other World', 54.

Sugar, O. 1987. 'How the Sacrum Got Its Name'. *JAMA* 257 (15): 2061–63.

Summers, Anthony. 2015. 'Accessory Ossicles and Sesamoid Bones: Recognition and Treatment: Anthony Summers Explains How Emergency Nurse Practitioners Can Recognise Two Common Bone Variants in X-Rays of the Foot and Ankle That Are Often Mistaken for Fracture'. *Emergency Nurse* 22 (10): 27–32.

Taylor, Robert B. 2017. *The Amazing Language of Medicine: Understanding Medical Terms and Their Backstories*. Cham: Springer International Publishing.

Tekiner, Halil. 2015. 'A Cultural History of the Turkish Saddle'. *Journal of Turkish Studies* 10 (Volume 10 Issue 5): 319–319.

Tekiner, Halil, Niyazi Acer, and Fahrettin Kelestimur. 2015. 'Sella Turcica: An Anatomical, Endocrinological, and Historical Perspective'. *Pituitary* 18 (4): 575–78.

Wang, Lizhen, Jason Tak-Man Cheung, Fang Pu, Deyu Li, Ming Zhang, and Yubo Fan. 2011. 'Why Do Woodpeckers Resist Head Impact Injury: A Biomechanical Investigation'. *PLoS ONE* 6 (10).

Witcombe, Brian, and Dan Meyer. 2006. 'Sword Swallowing and Its Side Effects'. *BMJ: British Medical Journal* 333 (7582): 1285–87.

Wood, Gerald L. 1982. *The Guinness Book of Animal Facts and Feats*. 3rd ed. Enfield, Middlesex: Guinness Superlatives.

Zampieri, Fabio, Mohamed ElMaghawry, Alberto Zanatta, and Gaetano Thiene. 2015. 'Andreas Vesalius: Celebrating 500 Years of Dissecting Nature'. *Global Cardiology Science & Practice* 2015 (5).

Websites

https://www2.aston.ac.uk/lss/research/lss-research/ccisc/discourse-and-culture/west-midlands-english-speech-and-society/sounds-of-english/sound-production/index.aspx.

https://www2.palomar.edu/users/ccarpenter/Anatomywords.htm'.

https://www.bustle.com/articles/137763-Why-Are-High-Cheekbones-Considered-Attractive'.

https://www.dartmouth.edu/~humananatomy/resources/etymology.htm.

https://en.wikiversity.org/wiki/Latin/Colors.

https://en.wikipedia.org/w/index.php?title=List_of_medical_roots,_suffixes_and_prefixes&oldid=970453178.

https://www.etymonline.com/

https://eveappeal.org.uk/news-awareness/know-your-body/knowyourbody-test-knowledge/.

https://www.independent.co.uk/life-style/health-and-families/health-news/vagina-study-nearly-half-british-women-cannot-identify-vulva-cervix-a7219656.html.

https://www.independent.co.uk/voices/top-10-backformations-eytmology-A8766026.Html'.

https://www.merriam-webster.com/

https://metymology.ch/

https://www.pbs.org/wgbh/nova/article/flatfish-evolution/

https://www.scienceabc.com/humans/Why-Are-Lips-Different-from-Skin-Areas.Html'.

http://www.unifr.ch/ifaa/Public/EntryPage/HomePublicNew.html

https://yougov.co.uk/topics/health/articles-reports/2019/03/08/half-brits-dont-know-where-vagina-and-its-not-just.

https://www.youtube.com/watch?V=UixU1oRW64Q.

https://www.wikipedia.org/: the entire encyclopaedia

Legal Deposit January 2021

Lightning Source UK Ltd.
Milton Keynes UK
UKHW051558281022
411261UK00010B/62

9 782957 484706